TO PLAY MAN NUMBER ONE

compiled by Sara Hannum
and John Terry Chase

illustrated by Erwin Schachner

ATHENEUM   1971   NEW YORK

TO OUR PARENTS

Copyright © 1969 by Sara Hannum
and John Terry Chase
All rights reserved
Library of Congress catalog card number 73-75518
Published simultaneously in Canada by
McClelland and Stewart, Ltd.
Manufactured in the United States of America
by The Kingsport Press, Inc., Kingsport, Tennessee
Designed by Judith Lerner
First Printing August 1969
Second Printing September 1971

ACKNOWLEDGMENTS

THANKS ARE DUE to the following publishing companies, in the U.S. and abroad, and also to literary agencies and individuals for permission to reprint material found in *To Play Man Number One*.

Atheneum House, Inc. "Lizards and Snakes" from *The Hard Hours* by Anthony E. Hecht. Copyright © 1967 by Anthony E. Hecht. Reprinted by permission of Atheneum.

Shirley Bridges, author of "Imaginary Figures of the Virtues: Faith, by Roy Lichtenstein." First published in *The Kenyon Review*, and used by their permission and the author's.

Jonathan Cape, Ltd. "The Unexploded Bomb" from *The Gate* by Cecil Day Lewis. Reprinted by permission of Jonathan Cape, Ltd.

Collins-Knowlton-Wing, Inc. "From the Embassy" and "Nobody" from *Collected Poems*, published by Doubleday. Copyright © 1955 by Robert Graves. Reprinted by permission of Collins-Knowlton-Wing, Inc.

Curtis Brown Ltd. "An Adventure with a Lady," "The Assassin," "Self-Portrait as a Bear," "The Old Pilot's Death," from *A Roof of Tiger Lilies*, published by Viking Press. Copyright © 1964 by Donald Hall, reprinted by permission of Curtis Brown Ltd.

The Dial Press. "Sacrifice of a Rainbow Trout." Reprinted from *The Wheel of Summer* by Joseph Langland. Copyright © 1963, 1962, 1961, 1960, 1959, 1958, 1957, 1956, 1954, 1953, 1952, 1951, 1944 by Joseph Langland and used by permission of the publisher, The Dial Press, Inc.

Doubleday and Company, Inc. "Night Journey," Copyright 1940 by Theodore Roethke from *The Collected Poems of Theodore Roethke*. Reprinted by permission of Doubleday and Company, Inc. "Ombres Chinoises" from the book *Collected Poems* by Babette Deutsch. Copyright © 1969 by Babette Deutsch. Reprinted by permission of Doubleday and Company, Inc.

Alan Dugan. "Portrait," Copyright © 1961 by Alan Dugan. First appeared in *Poems*, published by Yale University Press. Reprinted by permission of the author.

E. P. Dutton & Co., Inc. "Water Music," from the book *Collected Poems* by Lawrence Durrell. Copyright © 1956, 1960 by Lawrence Durrell. Reprinted by permission of E. P. Dutton and Co., Inc.

Faber and Faber Ltd. "A Trucker" and "Rastignac at 45" from *My Sad Captains* by Thom Gunn, reprinted by permission of Faber and Faber Ltd. "Water Music" from *Collected Poems* by Lawrence Durrell. Reprinted by permission of Faber and Faber Ltd. from *Collected Poems*. "Brother Fire" from *Collected Poems* by Louis MacNeice. Reprinted by permission of Faber and Faber Ltd. from *Collected Poems*.

Farrar, Straus and Giroux, Inc. "Metamorphoses" and "A Pilot from the Carrier" from *Complete Poems* by Randall Jarrell, Copyright © 1945, 1951, 1955 by Randall Jarrell, Copyright © 1969 by Mrs. Randall Jarrell. "The Mouth of the Hudson" and "Fall 1961" from *For the Union Dead* by Robert Lowell, Copyright © 1962, 1964 by Robert Lowell. Reprinted with the permission of Farrar, Straus and Giroux, Inc.

Grove Press, Inc. "Guerrilla Camp" from *Graves Registry and Other Poems* by Keith Wilson. Copyright © 1969 by Keith Wilson. Reprinted by permission of Grove Press, Inc.

v

Table of
CONTENTS

xii

A MILLION PEOPLE ON ONE STRING
THE TRAGEDY OF WAR   73

TO LAY HIS BRAIN UPON THE BOARD
POEMS OF CONFESSION   91

BEYOND THE COMPASS OF CHANGE
THE WONDERS OF LIFE AND DEATH 113

PERCEIVED IN A FINAL ATMOSPHERE

REFLECTIONS ON THE HUMAN CONDITION

POETS HAVE ALWAYS been moved to write about the human condition: society and its mores, the uniqueness and incomprehensibility of each person, the delight and the agony of love, the shock and the tragedy of war, the mysteries of birth, growth, dissolution, and death, the joy and guilt of self-awareness, the search for ultimate meaning.

Although the contemporary poet, like the great poets of the past, has addressed himself to these perennial human concerns, he has done so with a difference. He has spoken with a new voice. As Wallace Stevens put it, he has played his ancient song on a new instrument, a blue guitar. In the opening stanza of *The Man with the Blue Guitar*, the musician's audience complains (like the rest of the modern world which is disturbed to find itself no longer anchored to tradition or to the familiar) that the poet does not "play things as they are." The poet answers, "Things as they are are changed upon the blue guitar." Soon his listeners sense that the blue guitar, that is the poetic imagination, has not distorted reality, but instead has presented truth. "Play you must," they say, "a tune beyond us, yet ourselves, a tune upon the blue guitar of things exactly as they are."

Each of the poets represented in this anthology has his own style, his own blue guitar. Yet for all their differences, these poets speak with a voice that belongs to our own time and to no other. Like the poet of *The Man with the Blue Guitar*, contemporary poets cannot bring the "world quite round," patch it as they can. Nor can they glibly speak of heroes, but must "reach through" the past to "man," even if this means "to lay his brain upon the board and pick the acrid colors out." In short, contemporary poets have dared "to play man number one," to tell the truth, however "jan-gling" about modern men, "all their manner, right and wrong, and all their manner weak and strong."

Surely this kind of realism is of value in an age buffeted by violence and bewildered by the blandishments of adver-tising. As George Kennan, diplomat and historian, said be-fore the Academy of Arts and Letters: "The artists' duty is to lend to the comprehension of the human predicament a deeper dimension of insight in the light of which new pos-sibilities for self-fulfillment will be revealed and the tragic illusions of power and anger will lose their force."

To Wallace Stevens we wish to acknowledge our debt. From *The Man with the Blue Guitar* we have taken both the title and the section titles for this anthology. A final comment: Our intention has never been to make this an encyclopedia of contemporary verse. Instead we sought to present a powerful and imaginative collection of poems on the condition of modern man. All said and done now seemed the time, *To Play Man Number One*.

JOHN TERRY CHASE
SARA HANNUM
New York 1969

TO PLAY MAN NUMBER ONE

Wallace Stevens
THE MAN WITH THE BLUE GUITAR

I

The man bent over his guitar,
A shearsman of sorts. The day was green.

They said, "You have a blue guitar,
You do not play things as they are."

The man replied, "Things as they are
Are changed upon the blue guitar."

And they said then, "But play, you must,
A tune beyond us, yet ourselves,

A tune upon the blue guitar
Of things exactly as they are."

II

I cannot bring a world quite round,
Although I patch it as I can.

I sing a hero's head, large eye
And bearded bronze, but not a man,

Although I patch him as I can
And reach through him almost to man.

If to serenade almost to man
Is to miss, by that, things as they are,

Say that it is the serenade
Of a man that plays a blue guitar.

III

Ah, but to play man number one,
To drive the dagger in his heart,

To lay his brain upon the board
And pick the acrid colors out,

To nail his thought across the door,
Its wings spread wide to rain and snow,

To strike his living hi and ho,
To tick it, tock it, turn it true,

To bang it from a savage blue,
Jangling the metal of the strings . . .

IV

So that's life, then: things as they are?
It picks its way on the blue guitar.

A million people on one string?
And all their manner in the thing.

And all their manner, right and wrong.
And all their manner, weak and strong?

The feelings crazily, craftily call,
Like a buzzing of flies in autumn air,

And that's life, then: things as they are,
This buzzing of the blue guitar.

V

Do not speak to us of the greatness of poetry,
Of the torches wisping in the underground,

Of the structure of vaults upon a point of light.
There are no shadows in our sun,

Day is desire and night is sleep.
There are no shadows anywhere.

The earth, for us, is flat and bare.
There are no shadows. Poetry

Exceeding music must take the place
Of empty heaven and its hymns,

Ourselves in poetry must take their place,
Even in the chattering of your guitar.

VI

A tune beyond us as we are,
Yet nothing changed by the blue guitar;

Ourselves in the tune as if in space,
Yet nothing changed, except the place

Of things as they are and only the place
As you play them, on the blue guitar,

Placed so, beyond the compass of change,
Perceived in a final atmosphere;

For a moment final, in the way
The thinking of art seems final when

The thinking of the god is smoky dew.
The tune is space. The blue guitar

Becomes the place of things as they are,
A composing of senses of the guitar.

THE
BUZZING
OF THE
BLUE GUITAR

Poems of the Modern World

Barbara Howes
CITY AFTERNOON

Far, far down
The earth rumbles in sleep;
Up through its iron grille,
The subway, black as a chimney—
Sweep, growls. An escalator rides
On dinosaur spines
Toward day. And on beyond,
Old bones, bottles,
A dismantled piano, sets
Of Mrs. Humphrey Ward all whirl
In the new disposal-unit; above
Its din, apartments are tenanted
Tight as hen-houses, people roosting
In every cupboard. Eighty storeys
Up, pigeons nest on the noise
Or strut above it; higher,
The outcast sun serves its lean meat
Of light.

The whinnying
Of Venetian blinds has ceased: we sit
Invisible in this room,
Behind glass. In a lull,
A chance abatement of sound, a scalping
Silence, far
Down we hear the Iron
Maiden whisper,
Closing upon her spikes.

Richard Wilbur
A FIRE-TRUCK

Right down the shocked street with a siren-blast
That sends all else skittering to the curb,
Redness, brass, ladders and hats hurl past,
   Blurring to sheer verb,

Shift at the corner into uproarious gear
And make it around the turn in a squall of traction,
The headlong bell maintaining sure and clear,
   Thought is degraded action!

Beautiful, heavy, unweary, loud, obvious thing!
I stand here purged of nuance, my mind a blank.
All I was brooding upon has taken wing,
   And I have you to thank.

As you howl beyond hearing I carry you into my mind,
Ladders and brass and all, there to admire
Your phoenix-red simplicity, enshrined
   In that not extinguished fire.

May Swenson
THE CONTRAPTION

      Going up is pleasant. It tips your chin,
         and you feel tall and free
      as if in control of, and standing in
      a chariot, hands feeling the frisky

reins. But, doubled in your seat,
knuckled to the fun-car's handrails,
you mount baby-buggied, cleat by cleat,
to that humped apogee your entrails

aren't ready for. Wind in your
ears, clouds in your eyes, it's easy
to define the prophetic jelly at your core
as joy. The landscape of amusement goes queasy

only when the gilded buckboard juts straight out
over undippered air. A jaw of horror will spill
you? Not yet. The route
becomes a roaring trough for the next hill

hairpinning higher. You wish you had
the chance to count how many ups,
downs and switchbacks the mad
rattler, rearing its steep hoops, has. The divan hiccups

over a straightaway now, at mild speed.
Then you look: Jolly carousel and ferris wheel, far
years beneath, are cruel gears you can be emptied
into over the side of the hellish sled. Star-

beaded sky! (It feels better to look higher.) How
did the morning, the whole blue-and-white day
go by in what seems one swoop? You vow
to examine the contraption and its fairway,

measure the system of gruesome twists,
the queer dimensions, if ever you get down. Going
down is a dull road. Your fists
loosen, pretend no longer, knowing

they grip no stick of purpose. The final chutes are
unspectacular, slower repetitious of past
excitements. A used and vulgar car
shovels you home in a puzzling gloom. The vast

agitation faded in your bowels, you think
that from the ground you'll trace the rim
your coaster sped and crawled, the sink
and rise, the reason for its shape. Grim

darkness now. The ride
is complete. You are positioned for discovery, but,
your senses gone, you can't see the upper arching works. Wide
silence. Midnight. The carnival is shut.

Robert Lowell
THE MOUTH OF THE HUDSON
(FOR ESTHER BROOKS)

A single man stands like a bird-watcher,
and scuffles the pepper and salt snow
from a discarded, gray
Westinghouse Electric cable drum.
He cannot discover America by counting
the chains of condemned freight-trains
from thirty states. They jolt and jar
and junk in the siding below him.
He has trouble with his balance.
His eyes drop,
and he drifts with the wild ice
ticking seaward down the Hudson,
like the blank sides of a jig-saw puzzle.

The ice ticks seaward like a clock.
A Negro toasts
wheat-seeds over the coke-fumes
of a punctured barrel.
Chemical air
sweeps in from New Jersey,
and smells of coffee.

Across the river,
ledges of suburban factories tan
in the sulphur-yellow sun
of the unforgivable landscape.

Philip Booth
CHOOSING A HOMESITE

If possible, choose a lot
not already surveyed
for next fall's Thruway, not

this spring to be conveyed
to the Commissioner of Parks,
or on the Instrument

Approach of Mach-3 jets
(although your own rights
will be, always, defended

in any case of Eminent
Domain, or Public Works)
when the next runway is extended.

13

Since conscience might, of course,
commit you to a new State
Asylum, you could do worse,

in truth, than finance a lot
in some strategically optioned, still-
to-be-paved development; a last

choice, yes, but zoned, green,
and *No Cash Down*
for paraplegic veterans. Prices

are high, but consider the cost
of moving up: say to a hill-
top thick with scanning devices.

Big fields are good, but beware
the silo housing a hybrid
missile. Search your deed,

if you choose the coast, for sub-pens
under your frontage. A lot
will depend, too, on what happens

overhead. The apple valleys,
upstate, are heavy with millicuries.
If you bear children, share

your mortgage with them: they,
or their children, will have to pay
if real estate booms. Whatever homesite

you choose, you'll be taxed to play hero.
Now that the bombsight is obsolete,
today's best buy is Ground Zero.

Langston Hughes
BALLAD OF THE LANDLORD

Landlord, landlord,
My roof has sprung a leak.
Don't you 'member I told you about it
Way last week?

Landlord, landlord,
These steps is broken down.
When you come up yourself
It's a wonder you don't fall down.

Ten bucks you say I owe you?
Ten bucks you say is due?
Well, that's Ten Bucks more'n I'll pay you
Till you fix this house up new.

What? You gonna get eviction orders?
You gonna cut off my heat?
You gonna take my furniture and
Throw it in the street?

Um-huh! You talking high and mighty.
Talk on—till you get through.
You ain't gonna be able to say a word
If I land my fist on you.

15

Police! Police!
Come and get this man!
He's trying to ruin the government
And overturn the land!

Copper's whistle!
Patrol bell!
Arrest.

Precinct Station.
Iron cell.
Headlines in press:

MAN THREATENS LANDLORD

TENANT HELD NO BAIL

JUDGE GIVES NEGRO 90 DAYS IN COUNTY JAIL

Howard Nemerov
THE DAILY GLOBE

Each day another installment of the old
Romance of Order brings to the breakfast table
The paper flowers of catastrophe.
One has this recurrent dream about the world.

Headlines declare the ambiguous oracles,
The comfortable old prophets mutter doom.
Man's greatest intellectual pleasure is
To repeat himself, yet somehow the daily globe

16

Rolls on, while the characters in comic strips
Prolong their slow, interminable lives
Beyond the segregated photographs
Of the girls that marry and the men that die.

Richard Wilbur
STATUES

These children playing at statues fill
The gardens with their shrillness; in a planned
And planted grove they fling from the swinger's hand
Across the giddy grass and then hold still

In gargoyle attitudes,—as if
All definition were outrageous. Then
They melt in giggles and begin again.
Above their heads the maples with a stiff

Compliance entertain the air
In abrupt gusts, losing the look of trees
In rushed and cloudy metamorphoses,
Their shadows all a brilliant disrepair,

A wash of dodging stars, through which
The children weave and then again undo
Their fickle zodiacs. It is a view
lively as Ovid's Chaos, and its rich

Uncertainty compels the crowd:
Two nuns regard it with habitual love,
Moving along a path as mountains move
Or seem to move when traversed by a cloud;

The soldier breaks his iron pace;
Linked lovers pause to gaze; and every role
Relents,—until the feet begin to stroll
Or stride again. But settled in disgrace

Upon his bench, one aging bum,
Brought by his long evasion and distress
Into an adamantine shapelessness,
Stares at the image of his kingdom come.

Langston Hughes
HARLEM

What happens to a dream deferred?

Does it dry up
like a raisin in the sun?
Or fester like a sore—
And then run?
Does it stink like rotten meat?
Or crust and sugar over—
Like a syrupy sweet?

Maybe it just sags
Like a heavy load.

Or does it explode?

Gwendolyn Brooks
THE POOL PLAYERS,
SEVEN AT THE GOLDEN SHOVEL
WE REAL COOL

We real cool. We
Left school. We

Lurk late. We
Strike straight. We

Sing sin. We
Thin gin. We

Jazz June. We
die soon.

David Wagoner
THE HOLD-UP

First comes a fence, then the mouth of an alley,
Then a shadow on the other side of shadows
Becomes a pole, a doorway, a garbage can
Becoming a bush with a voice becoming an arm
Holding a gun at my back. This is a hold-up.
We wait a moment. We listen
For whatever it might be I'm going to say.
The wind crawls out from under the parked cars.

My arms go up in the air. My hands turn white.
Apparently I won't be saying anything.

He touches the empty pocket over my heart,
Then pats my hips as if guessing my weight.
Half-turning, I see the stocking over his face
Erasing eyes and lips, smoothing his nose.
We pass the time of night together.
He does the breathing for both of us.

The muzzle touches my back
Gently, like the muzzle of a dog. What's holding me up?
Take off your shoes. I stand in stocking feet
On the cinders. He begins to fade.
I had been walking from streetlight to streetlight,
My shadow straight as a footbridge under me,
Forgetting the mouths of alleys by moonlight.
My shoes and my money are running away in the dark.

Rod McKuen
BROWNSTONE

Birds and butterflies
dart
    down
        canyons
between tall buildings
looking for a place to hide
as the sky above the city darkens
and the rain begins
        timid at first—unsure
then creeping onto window ledges
and foraging along the sidewalk.

They're tearing down the building across the street
and the old woman who sat cushion high
behind the flower boxes
                              is gone.
Even the children who played along the broken sidewalk
                              have disappeared
and their hop-scotch lines are washed away.

Only the multi-colored cat
preening in the shop window
is unconcerned
as night begins.

Marya Zaturenska
FLIGHT OF THE SPARROWS

Sparrows through the winters flying
Over misted roof and sky,
Clinging to the wind and sighing
In a gray immensity,

The immense sky and towers,
While below the small, brown lives
Crawl in time, the whirling hours
Burned away in narrow hives.

Then the soul in indignation
Tore its frantic way in flight
To fantastic contemplation
Of the splendors of the night.

Dreamed of peacocks, glittering, gold,
Trees whose happy branches spread
Into landscapes free and bold—
Expanding daystreams overhead.

Slowly, slowly, year by year,
In an angry flight defying,
You escape—return to clear
Cold winters where the sparrows veer,

Through the desperate city flying.

Sylvia Plath
BALLOONS

Since Christmas they have lived with us,
Guileless and clear,
Oval soul-animals,
Taking up half the space,
Moving and rubbing on the silk

Invisible air drifts,
Giving a shriek and pop
When attacked, then scooting to rest, barely trembling.
Yellow cathead, blue fish—
Such queer moons we live with

Instead of dead furniture!
Straw mats, white walls
And these travelling
Globes of thin air, red, green,
Delighting

The heart like wishes or free
Peacocks blessing
Old ground with a feather
Beaten in starry metals.
Your small

Brother is making
His balloon squeak like a cat.
Seeming to see
A funny pink world he might eat on the other side of it,
He bites,

Then sits
Back, fat jug
Contemplating a world clear as water,
A red
Shred in his little fist.

David Ignatow
SIMULTANEOUSLY

Simultaneously, five thousand miles apart,
two telephone poles, shaking and roaring
and hissing gas, rose from their emplacements
straight up, leveled off and headed
for each other's land, alerted radar
and ground defense, passed each other
in midair, escorted by worried planes,
and plunged into each other's place,
steaming and silent and standing straight,
sprouting leaves.

Babette Deutsch
OMBRES CHINOISES

The city misted in rain, dim wet flashes of light
Strike through the dusk; vague thunderings—a train.
Over the street's glimmer the cabs rattle and slip;
Darkly the pavement's shine
Reaches into the night.
On blackness color flames: purple and blurs of red
Like fruits of faery bloom,
Yellow soft as honey and gold,
Green as though crushed emeralds bled,
Arctic blue in pale cold ribbons
Lost in fume.

Wind, and those shaken lanterns are swept off
By the shadows' broom.

Richard Lattimore
AMERICAN NIGHTS

I

This is a world of picket fences, knowing
the girls pass arm in arm from up the courthouse square
down to the soda parlor, hears them throwing
the fragments of their laughter down the dark
and summer-close and elm-grown small town air.
The bandstand in the middle of the park
watches lank adolescents swing their cars
with languid fingers into cruel curves,

reverse and start and wipe the night with stars,
and take the road, this ribbon world of nerves
driving forever driving in a dream
of black escape from automobile eyes.
On either hand the backyard landscapes stream
as flight in fluid haste, and memory-wise.

Theodore Roethke
NIGHT JOURNEY

Now as the train bears west,
Its rhythm rocks the earth,
And from my Pullman berth
I stare into the night
While others take their rest.
Bridges of iron lace,
A suddenness of trees,
A lap of mountain mist
All cross my line of sight,
Then a bleak wasted place,
And a lake below my knees.
Full on my neck I feel
The straining at a curve;
My muscles move with steel,
I wake in every nerve.
I watch a beacon swing
From dark to blazing bright;
We thunder through ravines
And gullies washed with light.
Beyond the mountain pass
Mist deepens on the pane;

We rush into a rain
That rattles double glass.
Wheels shake the roadbed stone,
The pistons jerk and shove,
I stay up half the night
To see the land I love.

Thom Gunn
A TRUCKER

Sometimes it is like a beast
barely controlled by a man.
But the cabin is lofty
as a skull, and all the rest
extends from his foot as an
enormous throbbing body:

if he left anything to
chance—see his great frame capsize,
and his rubber limbs explode
whirling! and see there follow
a bright fountain of red eyes
tinkling sightless to the road.

John Updike
SONIC BOOM

I'm sitting in the living room,
When, up above, the Thump of Doom
Resounds. Relax. It's sonic boom.

The ceiling shudders at the clap,
The mirrors tilt, the rafters snap,
And Baby wakens from his nap.

"Hush, babe. Some pilot we equip,
Giving the speed of sound the slip,
Has cracked the air like a penny whip."

Our world is far from frightening; I
No longer strain to read the sky
Where moving fingers (jet planes) fly.
Our world seems much too tame to die.

And if it does, with one more *pop*,
I shan't look up to see it drop.

Robert Bly
WATCHING TELEVISION

Sounds are heard too high for ears,
From the body cells there is an answering bay;
Soon the inner streets fill with a chorus of barks.

We see the landing craft coming in,
The black car sliding to a stop,
The Puritan killer loosening his guns.

Wild dogs tear off noses and eyes
And run off with them down the street—
The body tears off its own arms and throws them into the air.

The detective draws fifty-five million people into his revolver,
Who sleep restlessly as in an air raid in London;
Their backs become curved in the sloping dark.

The filaments of the soul slowly separate:
The spirit breaks, a puff of dust floats up,
Like a house in Nebraska that suddenly explodes.

Carl Sandburg
MR. ATTILA

They made a myth of you, professor,
    you of the gentle voice,
    the books, the specs,
    the furtive rabbit manners
    in the mortar-board cap
    and the medieval gown.

They didn't think it, eh professor?
On account of you're so absent-minded,
you bumping into the tree and saying,
"Excuse me, I thought you were a tree,"
passing on again blank and absent-minded.

Now it's "Mr. Attila, how do you do?"
Do you pack wallops of wholesale death?
Are you the practical dynamic son-of-a-gun?
Have you come through with a few abstractions?
Is it you Mr. Attila we hear saying,
"I beg your pardon but we believe we have made some degree
    of progress on the residual qualities of the atom"?

AUGUST, 1945

C. D. Lewis
THE UNEXPLODED BOMB

Two householders (semi-detached) once found,
Digging their gardens, a bomb underground—
Half in one's land, half in t'others, with the fence between.

Neighbors they were, but for years had been
Hardly on speaking terms. Now X. unbends
To pass a remark across the creosoted fence:
'Look what I've got!'
                  'Oh, you've got it too.
Then what, may I ask, are you proposing to do
About this object of yours which menaces my wife,
My kiddies, my property, my whole way of life?'
'Your way of life,' says Y., 'is no credit to humanity.
I don't wish to quarrel; but, since you began it, I
Find your wife stuck-up, your children repel me,
And let me remind you that we too have the telly.
This bomb of mine—'
               'I don't like your tone!
And I must point out that, since I own
More bomb than you, to create any tension
Between us won't pay you.'
              'What a strange misapprehension!'
Says the other: 'my portion of bomb is near
Six inches longer than yours. So there!'

'They seem,' the bomb muttered in its clenched and narrow
Sleep, 'to take me for a vegetable marrow.'

'It would give me,' said X., 'the very greatest pleasure
To come across the fence now with my tape-measure—'

'Oh no,' Y. answered, 'I'm not having you
Trampling my flowerbeds and peering through
My windows.'
                    'Oho,' snarled X., 'if that's
Your attitude, I warn you to keep your brats
In future from trespassing upon my land,
Or they'll bitterly regret it.'
                'You misunderstand.
My family has no desire to step on
Your soil; and my bomb is a peace-lover's weapon.

Called a passing angel, 'If you two shout
And fly into tantrums and keep dancing about,
The thing will go off. It is surely permissible
To say that your bomb, though highly fissible,
Is in another sense one and indivisible;
By which I mean—if you'll forgive the phrase,
Gentlemen—the bloody thing works both ways.
So let me put forth a dispassionate proposal:
Both of you, ring for a bomb-disposal
Unit, and ask them to remove post haste
The cause of your dispute.'
              X. and Y. stared aghast
At the angel. 'Remove my bomb?' they sang
In unison both: 'allow a gang
To invade my garden and pull up the fence
Upon which my whole way of life depends?
Only a sentimental idealist
Could moot it. I, thank God, am a realist.'

The angel fled. The bomb turned over
In its sleep and mumbled 'I shall soon discover,
If X. and Y. are too daft to unfuse me,
How the Devil intends to use me.'

Donald Hall
THE ASSASSIN

the spider glints
he is huge he is made of aluminum
slowly the crane lowers him
outside a glass building
his legs crawl in the air
he dangles turning
by a steel thread
the sun splits on his metal skin
no one sees him

I kneel at a wooden box
in shade in silence
eye-socket touches felt eyepiece
a car rolls slowly
into the crossed hairs
a head
enters the segments of a circle
hairs cross on a head
I squeeze slowly

the crane lifts the spider slowly
his legs retracting
he becomes a sphere a point
glinting aluminum
no one sees him
the crane swerves him over a ledge
his nest on a high building
humming in a cement hole
electric glass

Phyllis Masek Harris
FURNITURE

there are youngsters now
younger than I, moving as nomads
through the makeshift camping grounds

who do not hope for what was
expected: the catalog comforts
of minor success

nor do they imagine
changelessness, that what they encounter
remains

whose parents
in the suburbs, in the small
midwestern towns

have set down heavy houses on the land
& filled them
with a weight of furnishings, & in a manner
held them down

but not their children: who dreamed of Indians
tracking.
& move lightly, from city
to city

exchanging
adornments; themselves the only
shelter they have found

Adrienne Rich
A CHANGE OF WORLD

Fashions are changing in the sphere.
Oceans are asking wave by wave
What new shapes will be worn next year;
And the mountains stooped and grave,
Are wondering silently range by range
What if they prove too old for the change.

The little tailors busily sitting
Flashing their shears in rival haste
Won't spare the time for prior fitting—
In with the stitches, too late to baste.
They say the season for doubt has passed:
The changes coming are due to last.

I SING
A HERO'S
HEAD

Portraits in Poetry

John Updike
EX-BASKETBALL PLAYER

Pearl Avenue runs past the high-school lot,
Bends with the trolley tracks, and stops, cut off
Before it has a chance to go two blocks,
At Colonel McComsky Plaza. Bert's Garage
Is on the corner facing west, and there,
Most days, you'll find Flick Webb, who helps Bert out.

Flick stands tall among the idiot pumps—
Five on a side, the old bubble-head style,
Their rubber elbows hanging loose and low.
One's nostrils are two S's, and his eyes
An E and O. And one is squat, without
A head at all—more of a football type.

Once Flick played for the high-school team, the Wizards.
He was good: in fact, the best. In '46
He bucketed three hundred ninety points,
A county record still. The ball loved Flick.
I saw him rack up thirty-eight or forty
In one home game. His hands were like wild birds.

He never learned a trade, he just sells gas,
Checks oil, and changes flats. Once in a while,
As a gag, he dribbles an inner tube,
But most of us remember anyway.
His hands are fine and nervous on the lug wrench.
It makes no difference to the lug wrench, though.

Off work, he hangs around Mae's luncheonette.
Grease-gray and kind of coiled, he plays pinball,

37

Sips lemon cokes and smokes those thin cigars;
Flick seldom speaks to Mae, just sits and nods
Beyond her face toward bright applauding tiers
Of Necco Wafers, Nibs, and JuJu Beads.

Anthony Hecht
LIZARDS AND SNAKES

On the summer road that ran by our front porch
    Lizards and snakes came out to sun.
It was hot as a stove out there, enough to scorch
    A buzzard's foot. Still, it was fun
To lie in the dust and spy on them. Near but remote,
    They snoozed in the carriage ruts, a smile
In the set of the jaw, a fierce pulse in the throat
Working away like Jack Doyle's after he'd run the mile.

Aunt Martha had an unfair prejudice
    Against them (as well as being cold
Toward bats.) She was pretty inflexible in this,
    Being a spinster and all, and old.
So we used to slip them into her knitting box.
    In the evening she'd bring in things to mend
And a nice surprise would slide out from under the socks.
It broadened her life, as Joe said. Joe was my friend.

But we never did it again after the day
    Of the big wind when you could hear the trees
Creak like rockingchairs. She was looking away
    Off, and kept saying, "Sweet Jesus, please
Don't let him near me. He's as like as twins.
    He can crack us like lice with his fingernail.

I can see him plain as a pikestaff. Look how he grins
And swings the scaly horror of his folded tail."

James Wright
TO A FUGITIVE

The night you got away, I dreamed you rose
Out of the earth to lean on a young tree.
Then they were there, hulking the moon away,
The great dogs rooting, snuffing up the grass.
You raise a hand, hungry to hold your lips
Out of the wailing air; but lights begin
Spidering the ground; oh they come closing in,
The beam searches your face like fingertips.

Hurry, Maguire, hammer the body down,
Crouch to the wall again, shackle the cold
Machine guns and the sheriff and the cars:
Divide the bright bars of the cornered bone,
Strip, run for it, break the last law, unfold,
Dart down the alley, race between the stars.

Kenneth Patchen
ALWAYS ANOTHER VIEWPOINT

You climb three "golden steps"
Past some friendly "lions"
And "the skeleton
of a king!" The "lions"

Belong to a woman

39

Who's said to
Be a bit off. Actually she's
A fine person. I
Think more misunderstood than mad.

I live next door

In the
House with the dwarfpalm trees
Growing
Up through the roof.
Over beer she tells me
Stories about
When she was a

Queen. On rainy nights.

Donald Justice
THE MISSING PERSON

He has come to report himself
A missing person.

The authorities
Hand him the forms.

He knows how they have waited
With the learned patience of barbers

In small shops, idle,
Stropping their razors.

40

But now that these spaces in his life
Stare up at him blankly,

Waiting to be filled in,
He does not know how to begin.

Afraid
That he may not answer even

To his description of himself,
He asks for a mirror.

They reassure him
That he can be nowhere

But wherever he finds himself
From moment to moment,

Which, for the moment, is here.
And he might like to believe them.

But in the mirror
He sees what is missing.

It is himself
He sees there emerging

Slowly, as from the dark
Of a furnished room

Only by dark,
One who receives no mail

And is known to the landlady only
For keeping himself to himself,

And for whom it will be years yet
Before he can trust to the light

This last disguise, himself.

Thom Gunn
RASTIGNAC AT 45

Here he is of course. It was his best
trick always: when we glance again toward
the shadow we see it has consist-
ed of him all along, lean and bored.

We denounced him so often! Yet he
comes up, and leans on one of the bars
in his dark suit, indicating the
empty glass as if we were waiters.

We fill it, and submit, more or less,
to his marvellous air of knowing
all the ropes debonair weariness
could care to handle, of "everything

that I know I know from having done,
child, and I survive." What calmly told
confidences of exploration
among the oversexed and titled,

or request for a few days' loan, are
we about to hear? Rastignac tell us
about Life, and what men of your
stamp endure. It must be terrible.

It is. To the left of his mouth is
an attractive scarlike line, not caused
by time unhelped. It is not the prize,
either, of a dueller's lucky thrust.

But this: time after time the fetid
taste to the platitudes of Romance
has drawn his mouth up to the one side
secretly, in a half-maddened wince.

We cannot help but pity him that
momentary convulsion; however,
the mere custom of living with it
has, for him, diminished the horror.

Donald Hall
THE OLD PILOT'S DEATH

He discovers himself on an old airfield.
He thinks he was there before,
but rain has washed out the lettering of a sign
A single biplane, all struts and wires,
stands in the long grass and wildflowers.
He pulls himself into the narrow cockpit
although his muscles are stiff
and sits like an egg in a nest of canvas.
He sees that the machine gun has rusted.

The glass over the instruments
has broken, and the red arrows are gone
from his gas gauge and his altimeter.
When he looks up, his propeller is turning,
although no one was there to snap it.
He lets out the throttle. The engine catches
and the propeller spins into the wind.
He bumps over holes in the grass,
and he remembers to pull back on the stick.
He rises from the land in a high bounce
which gets higher, and suddenly he is flying again.
He feels the old fear, and rising over the fields
the old gratitude. In the distance, circling
in a beam of late sun like birds migrating,
there are the wings of a thousand biplanes.
He banks and flies to join them.

IN MEMORY OF PHILIP THOMPSON, D. 1960

Richard Eberhart
A MAINE ROUSTABOUT

He was there as the yachts went by

Percy is my name; my accent is good,
I am told, as good as that of an Elizabethan.
I had no schooling beyond the age of sixteen.
My wife left me. I took to drink, live with a dog.
I resent children unless they can hold their own
With grown-ups. I've been around the world on ships,
Down Connecticut way on jobs, once got to Georgia,
Always return to the rocks and the hard times

44

Of Maine. At clambakes in the summertime
I sit with the summer folk on the conglomerate shore,
Play my fiddle a sharp tune or two,
Old airs I learned from my brother when we were boys.
It was always tough with me. Sharp as the city folks
I think I am, but am ever wary against them,
Keep my difference, and will not let them tell me off.
I have no respect for their savage villainies,
Yet their power over life always fascinated me.
They own the place. They come and go, I'm left
To chores and dung. But I can catch a mackerel
Almost any afternoon on the incoming tide
With an old hook, when they're running, old line,
In my old boat: they won't take hook from the richlings.
If I scare the children with my grizzled face
It's an old gut forced with whiskey keeps me going.

William Stafford
THE WOMAN AT BANFF

While she was talking a bear happened along, violating
every garbage can. Shaking its loose, Churchillian,
V for victory suit, it ripped up and ate
a greasy "Bears Are Dangerous!" sign.

While she was talking the trees above signalled—
"Few," and the rock back of them—"Cold."
And while she was talking a moose—huge, black—
swam that river and faded off winterward,

Up toward the Saskatchewan.

45

Gwendolyn Brooks
THE PARENTS: PEOPLE LIKE
OUR MARRIAGE
MAXIE AND ANDREW

Clogged and soft and sloppy eyes
Have lost the light that bites or terrifies.

There are no swans and swallows any more.
The people settled for chicken and shut the door.

But one by one
They got things done:
Watch for porches as you pass
And prim low fencing pinching in the grass.

Pleasant custards sit behind
The white Venetian blind.

Anne Sexton
THE ADDICT

Sleepmonger,
deathmonger,
with capsules in my palms each night,
eight at a time from sweet pharmaceutical bottles
I make arrangements for a pint-sized journey.
I'm the queen of this condition.
I'm an expert on making the trip
and now they say I'm an addict.
Now they ask why.
Why!

46

Don't they know
that I promised to die!
I'm keeping in practice.
I'm merely staying in shape.
The pills are a mother, but better,
every color and as good as sour balls.
I'm on a diet from death.

Yes, I admit
it has gotten to be a bit of a habit—
blows eight at a time, socked in the eye,
hauled away by the pink, the orange,
the green and white goodnights.
I'm becoming something of a chemical
mixture.
That's it!

My supply
of tablets
has got to last for years and years.
I like them more than I like me.
Stubborn as hell, they won't let go.
It's a kind of marriage.
It's a kind of war
where I plant bombs inside
of myself.

Yes
I try
to kill myself in small amounts,
an innocuous occupation.
Actually I'm hung up on it.
But remember I don't make too much noise.

And frankly no one has to lug me out
and I don't stand there in my winding sheet.
I'm a little buttercup in my yellow nightie
eating my eight loaves in a row
and in a certain order as in
the laying on of hands
or the black sacrament.

It's a ceremony
but like any other sport
it's full of rules.
It's like a musical tennis match where
my mouth keeps catching the ball.
Then I lie on my altar
elevated by the eight chemical kisses.

What a lay me down this is
with two pink, two orange,
two green, two white goodnights.
Fee-fi-fo-fum—
Now I'm borrowed.
Now I'm numb.

FIRST OF FEBRUARY, 1966

Alan Dugan
PORTRAIT

The captive flourished like
a mushroom in his oubliette.
He breathed his night's breath every day,
took food and water from the walls

and ruled his noisy rats and youth.
He made a calendar of darkness,
thought his boredom out, and carved
Heaven in his dungeon with a broken spoon.

At last he made his own
light like a deep sea fish, and when
his captors' children came for him
they found no madman in a filthy beard
or heap of rat-picked bones:
they found a spry, pale old gentleman
who had a light around his head.
Oh he could stare as well as ever,
argue in a passionate voice
and walk on to the next
detention in their stone dismay
unaided.

Langston Hughes
TRUMPET PLAYER

The Negro
With the trumpet at his lips
Has dark moons of weariness
Beneath his eyes
Where the smoldering memory
Of slave ships
Blazed to the crack of whips
About his thighs.

The Negro
With the trumpet at his lips

49

Has a head of vibrant hair
Tamed down,
Paten-leathered now
Until it gleams
Like jet—
Were jet a crown.

The music
From the trumpet at his lips
Is honey
Mixed with liquid fire.
The rhythm
From the trumpet at his lips
Is ecstasy
Distilled from old desire—

Desire
That is longing for the moon
Where the moonlight's but a spotlight
In his eyes,
Desire
That is longing for the sea
Where the sea's a bar-glass
Sucker size.

The Negro
With the trumpet at his lips
Whose jacket
Has a *fine* one-button roll,
Does not know
Upon what riff the music slips
Its hypodermic needle
To his soul—

But softly
As the tune comes from his throat
Trouble
Mellows to a golden note.

Adrienne Rich
AUNT JENNIFER'S TIGERS

Aunt Jennifer's tigers prance across a screen,
Bright topaz denizens of a world of green.
They do not fear the men beneath the tree;
They pace in sleek chivalric certainty.

Aunt Jennifer's fingers fluttering through her wool
Find even the ivory needle hard to pull.
The massive weight of Uncle's wedding band
Sits heavily upon Aunt Jennifer's hand.

When Aunt is dead, her terrified hands will lie
Still ringed with ordeals she was mastered by.
The tigers in the panel that she made
Will go on prancing, proud and unafraid.

Mark Van Doren
THE CAT AND THE MISER

Nothing could have brought him to the door,
This brown, this dripping night,
But the faint noise that did: a plucking,
Plucking at the tight
Copper crosswires of the screen.

5 1

He knew. It was the cat:
Her signal to come in.
Or thought he knew, the miser,
As with a groan, a sly grin,
Shuffling, he slid the bolt.

No eyes would have been so welcome,
Starring up and blinking.
But these, the tall thief's—
Oh, oh! the unthinking
Blow, the heavy feet.

Oh, oh! The boxes gone,
The misery. Then here she was:
Pluck, pluck—the sound,
In and out, of delicate claws.
What fiend had listened?

Out there, what sharpened face,
Vigilant, had learned the trick?
He staggered up and let her through.
Late, late! A sudden kick—
But then, caresses.

Adrienne Rich
FACE TO FACE

Never to be lonely like that—
the Early American figure on the beach
in black coat and knee-breeches
scanning the didactic storm in privacy,

never to hear the prairie wolves
in their lunar hilarity
circling one's little all, one's claim
to be Law and Prophets

for all that lawlessness,
never to whet the appetite
weeks early, for a face, a hand
longed-for and dreaded—

How people used to meet!
starved, intense, the old
Christmas gifts saved up till spring,
and the old plain words,

and each with his God-given secret,
spelled out through months of snow and silence,
burning under the bleached scalp; behind dry lips
a loaded gun.

1965

John Crowe Ransom
GOOD SHIPS

Fleet ships encountering on the high seas
Who speak, and then unto the vast diverge,
These hailed each other, poised on the loud surge
Of one of Mrs. Grundy's Tuesday teas,
Nor trimmed one sail to baffle the driving breeze.
A macaroon absorbed all her emotion;
His hue was ashy but an effect of ocean;
They exchanged the nautical technicalities.

53

It was only a nothing or so, and thus they parted.
Away they sailed, most certainly bound for port,
So seaworthy one felt they could not sink;
Still there was a tremor shook them, I should think,
Beautiful timbers fit for storm and sport
And unto miserly merchant hulks converted.

James Wright
A NOTE LEFT IN JIMMY LEONARD'S SHACK

Near the dry river's water-mark we found
    Your brother Minnegan,
Flopped like a fish against the muddy ground.
Beany, the kid whose yellow hair turns green,
Told me to find you, even in the rain,
    And tell you he was drowned.

I hid behind the chassis on the bank,
    The wreck of someone's Ford:
I was afraid to come and wake you drunk:
You told me once the waking up was hard,
The daylight beating at you like a board.
    Blood in my stomach sank.

Besides, you told him never to go out
    Along the river-side
Drinking and singing, clattering about.
You might have thrown a rock at me and cried
I was to blame, I let him fall in the road
    And pitch down on his side.

54

Well, I'll get hell enough when I get home
   For coming up this far,
Leaving the note, and running as I came.
I'll go and tell my father where you are.
You'd better go find Minnegan before
   Policemen hear and come.

Beany went home, and I got sick and ran,
   You old son of a bitch.
You better hurry down to Minnegan;
He's drunk or dying now, I don't know which,
Rolled in the roots and garbage like a fish,
   The poor old man.

   Gwendolyn Brooks
   JACK

         is not spendthrift of faith.
He has a skinny eye.
He spends a wariness of faith.
He puts his other by.

And comes it up his faith bought true,
He spends a little more.
And comes it up his faith bought false,
It's long gone from the store.

Jack Mathews
PARADIGM OF A HERO

One memory I have from childhood
is this: a heavy man trudging
in boots, ahead of me, a lantern
bumping at his knee. I remember
stepping over railroad ties
and staring at his broad back
as he walked ahead; I remember
the smoky wake of his tobacco,
the sound of his boots clomping
in the cinders, remember tiredness,
the smell of lateness in the night . . .
I remember the darkness
which each step spilled him into,
though I forget who he was,
or why we were walking
on that cold night. I remember
the warm lantern, clanking
against his leg, the darkness
all around, and the fact that
he never once paused, but stepped
like God himself, forward
into nothing, and into the past,
swinging his own casual light.

DAY
IS
DESIRE

Poems of Love

Marya Zaturenska
GIRL'S SONG

And always through my window pane
The shadow of a fine horseman riding
Over the dry plain.
Though in my heart it is green summer
I live in blossoming days
Always and always.

When will you descend,
Gay, smiling rider?
Delightful enemy, long-promised friend,
Spring from your saddle, moving toward my heart
Intent on murder or a kiss?
Here in the light I stand,
All summer in my hand.

My season sways with light,
Life streams from my round eyes,
Dreams with impassioned sight
See how the ripening fields remember me;
My feet are planted in full noon,
My words will blossom soon.

Though now they lie within my breast,
Heavy and dormant, shy and shivering
With what is unexpressed,
Soon they will melt the frozen throat in song
And locked rivers open, run
In the full mid-day sun.

Alastair Reid
THE DAY THE WEATHER BROKE

Last out in the raining weather, a girl and I
drip in the hazy light while cars slur by,
    and the single drizzling reason
    of rain in an alien season
turns us to each other till a train arrives,
to share, by bond of wetness, our wet lives.

Although, for talk, we can find to put our thumb on
    only the rain in common,
is this what love is—that we draw together
    in the inhuman weather,
Strangers, who pool our sheltered selves and take,
    for the sky's sake,
this luck, to be caught without our usual cloak
    the day the weather broke?

Lawrence Durrell
WATER MUSIC

Wrap your sulky beauty up,
From sea-fever, from winterfall
Out of the swing of the
Swing of the sea.

Keep safe from noonfall,
Starlight and smokefall where
Waves roll, waves toll but feel
None of our roving fever.

From dayfever and nightsadness
Keep, bless, hold: from cold
Wrap your sulky beauty into sleep
Out of the swing of the
Swing of sea.

James Dickey
SUN

O Lord, it was all night
Consuming me   skin crawling tighter than any
Skin of my teeth. Bleary with ointments, dazzling
Through the dark house   man red as iron   glowing
Blazing up anew with each bad
Breath from the bellowing curtains

I had held the sun longer
Than it could stay   and in the dark it turned
My face on, infra-red: there were cracks circling
My eyes where I had squinted
Up from stone-blind sand, and seen
Eternal fire   coronas   huge

Vertical banners of flame
Leap scrollingly from the sun and tatter
To nothing in blue-veined space
On the smoked-crimson glass of my lids.
When the sun fell, I slit my eyeskins
In the dazed ruddy muddle of twilight

And in the mirror saw whiteness
Run from my eyes like tears   going upward

And sideways   slanting   as well as falling,
All in straight lines like rays
Shining   and behind me, careful not
To touch without giving me a chance

To brace myself   a smeared
Suffering woman came merging her flame-shaken
Body halo with mine   her nose still clownish
With oxides: walked to me sweating
Blood, and turned around. I peeled off
Her bathing suit like her skin   her colors

Wincing   she silently biting
Her tongue off   her back crisscrossed with stripes
Where winter had caught her and whipped her.
We stumbled together, and in the double heat
The last of my blond hair blazed up,
Burned off me forever   as we dived

For the cool of the bed
In agony even at holding hands   the blisters
On our shoulders shifting   crackling
Releasing boiling water on the sheets. *O Lord*
Who can turn out the sun,   turn out that neighbor's
One bulb on his badminton court

For we are dying
Of light   searing each other   not able
To stop   to get away   she screaming O Lord
Apollo or Water, Water   as the moonlight drove
Us down on the tangled grid
Where in the end we lay

Suffering equally   in the sun
Backlashed from the moon's brutal stone
And meeting itself where we had stored it up
All afternoon in pain   in the gentlest touch
As we lay, O Lord,
In Hell, in love.

        e.e. cummings
            so shy shy shy (and with a

So shy shy shy (and with a
look the very boldest man
can scarcely dare to meet no matter

how he'll try to try)

So wrong (wrong wrong) and with a
smile at which the rightest man
remembers there is such a thing

as spring and wonders why

So gay gay gay and with a
wisdom not the wisest man
will partly understand (although

the wisest man am i)

So young young young and with a
something makes the oldest man
(whoever he may be) the only

man who'll never die

Jean Valentine
TO A FRIEND

I cannot give you much or ask you much.
Though I shore myself up until we meet,
The words we say are public as the street:
Your body is walled up against my touch.

Our ghosts bob and hug in the air where we meet,
My reason hinges on arcs you draw complete,
And yet you are walled up against my touch.

Your love for me is, in its way, complete,
Like alabaster apples angels eat,
But since it is in this world that we meet
I cannot give you much or ask you much.

You go your way, I mine, and when we meet,
Both half-distracted by the smells of the street,
Your body is walled up against my touch.

My body sings at your table, waits on the street
And you pass empty-handed, till when we meet
I have been so far, so deep, so cold, so much,
My hands, my eyes, my tongue are like bark to the touch.

Donald Hall
AN ADVENTURE WITH A LADY

As I watched, the animals
that lived in her shoulders
broke from their cages.

They prowled the room
with its ivory carvings.
They were lions!

They roared, and I thought
that I would be eaten
Well, I was ready,

but she shrugged her shoulders
and the wild lions
returned to their cages.

This heroine, this thicket
of lions smiled
between ivory earrings.

James Dickey
CHERRYLOG ROAD

Off Highway 106
At Cherrylog Road I entered
The '34 Ford without wheels,
Smothered in kudzu,
With a seat pulled out to run
Corn whiskey down from the hills,

And then from the other side
Crept into an Essex
With a rumble seat of red leather
And then out again, aboard
A blue Chevrolet, releasing
The rust from its other color,

65

Reared up on three building blocks.
None had the same body heat;
I changed with them inward, toward
The weedy heart of the junkyard,
For I knew that Doris Holbrook
Would escape from her father at noon

And would come from the farm
To seek parts owned by the sun
Among the abandoned chassis,
Sitting in each in turn
As I did, leaning forward
As in a wild stock-car race

In the parking lot of the dead.
Time after time, I climbed in
And out the other side, like
An envoy or movie star
Met at the station by crickets.
A radiator cap raised its head,

Became a real toad or kingsnake
As I neared the hub of the yard,
Passing through many states,
Many lives, to reach
Some grandmother's long Pierce-Arrow
Sending platters of blindness forth

From its nickel hubcaps
And spilling its tender upholstery
On sleepy roaches,
The glass panel in between
Lady and colored driver
Not all the way broken out,

The back-seat phone
Still on its hook.
I got in as though to explain,
"Let us go to the orphan asylum,
John; I have some old toys
For children who say their prayers."

I popped with sweat as I thought
I heard Doris Holbrook scrape
Like a mouse in the southern-state sun
That was eating the paint in blisters
From a hundred car tops and hoods.
She was tapping like code,

Loosening the screws,
Carrying off headlights,
Sparkplugs, bumpers,
Cracked mirrors and gear-knobs,
Getting ready, already,
To go back with something to show

Other than her lips' new trembling
I would hold to me soon, soon,
Where I sat in the ripped back seat
Talking over the interphone,
Praying for Doris Holbrook
To come from her father's farm

And to get back there
With no trace of me on her face
To be seen by her red-haired father
Who would change, in the squalling barn,
Her back's pale skin with a strop,
Then lay for me

In a bootlegger's roasting car
With a string-triggered 12-gauge shotgun
To blast the breath from the air.
Not cut by the jagged windshields,
Through the acres of wrecks she came
With a wrench in her hand,

Through dust where the blacksnake dies
Of boredom, and the beetle knows
The compost has no more life.
Someone outside would have seen
The oldest car's door inexplicably
Close from within:

I held her and held her and held her,
Convoyed at terrific speed
By the stalled, dreaming traffic around us,
So the blacksnake, stiff
With inaction, curved back
Into life, and hunted the mouse

With deadly overexcitement,
The beetles reclaimed their field
As we clung, glued together,
With the hooks of the seat springs
Working through to catch us red-handed
Amidst the gray breathless batting

That burst from the seat at our backs.
We left by separate doors
Into the changed, other bodies
Of cars, she down Cherrylog Road
And I to my motorcycle
Parked like the soul of the junkyard.

Restored, a bicycle fleshed
With power, and tore off
Up Highway 106, continually
Drunk on the wind in my mouth,
Wringing the handlebar for speed,
Wild to be wreckage forever.

Denise Levertov
FACE TO FACE

A nervous smile as gaze meets
gaze across
deep
river.
What place
for a smile here;
  it edges away

leaves us each at ravine's edge
alone with our bodies.

We plunge—
O dark river!
towards each other—
into that element—

a deep fall,
the eyes closing as if forever,
the air ripping, the waters
cleaving and closing upon us.

Heavy we are, our flesh
of stone and velvet goes down,
goes down.

Wallace Stevens
THE BEGINNING

So summer comes in the end to these few stains
And the rust and rot of the door through which she
    went.

The house is empty. But here is where she sat
To comb her dewy hair, a touchless light,

Perplexed by its darker iridescences.
This was the glass in which she used to look

At the moment's being, without history,
The self of summer perfectly perceived,

And feel its country gayety and smile
And be surprised and tremble, hand and lip.

This is the chair from which she gathered up
Her dress, the carefulest, commodious weave

Inwoven by a weaver to twelve bells . . .
The dress is lying, cast-off, on the floor.

Now, the first tutoyers of tragedy
Speak softly, to begin with, in the eaves.

James Wright
AUTUMNAL

Soft, where the shadow glides,
The yellow pears fell down.
The long bough slowly rides
The air of my delight.

Air, though but nothing, air
Falls heavy down your shoulder.
You hold in burdened hair
The color of my delight.

Neither the hollow pear,
Nor leaf among the grass,
Nor wind that wails the year
Against your leaning ear,
Will alter my delight:

That holds the pear upright
And sings along the bough,
Warms to the mellow sun.
The song of my delight
Gathers about you now,
Is whispered through, and gone.

A MILLION
PEOPLE ON
ONE
STRING

The Tragedy of War

Joseph Langland
WAR

When my young brother was killed
By a mute and dusty shell in the thorny bush
Crowning the boulders of the Villa Verde Trail
On the island of Luzon,

I laid my whole dry body down,
Dropping my face like a stone in a green park
On the east banks of the Rhine;

On an airstrip skirting the Seine
His sergeant brother sat like a stick in his barracks
While cracks of fading sunlight
Caged the dusty air;

In the rocky rolling hills west of the Mississippi
His father and mother sat in a simple Norwegian parlor
With a photograph smiling between them on the table
And their hands fallen into their laps
Like sticks and dust;

And still other brothers and sisters
Linking their arms together,
Walked down the dusty road where once he ran
And into the deep green valley
To sit on the stony banks of the stream he loved
And let the murmuring waters
Wash over their blood-hot feet with a springing crown of
    tears.

Louis Simpson
THE BATTLE

Helmet and rifle, pack and overcoat
Marched through a forest. Somewhere up ahead
Guns thudded. Like the circle of a throat
The night on every side was turning red.

They halted and they dug. They sank like moles
Into the clammy earth between the trees.
And soon the sentries, standing in their holes,
Felt the first snow. Their feet began to freeze.

At dawn the first shell landed with a crack.
Then shells and bullets swept the icy woods.
This lasted many days. The snow was black.
The corpses stiffened in their scarlet hoods.

Most clearly of that battle I remember
The tiredness in eyes, how hands looked thin
Around a cigarette, and the bright ember
Would pulse with all the life there was within.

Archibald MacLeish
WHAT THE OLD WOMEN SAY

Out there in the fighting
Each day is doubt,
Each night is dread,
Dawn is disaster.

Even at home in the house
If the lock creeps in the socket
The roots of our sleep wake.
We lie listening.

Like flood in a field it comes—
No sound but suddenly
One more stone has vanished,
A dyke drowned.

Never again in our lifetime,
Never will fear end
Or the old ease return to us:
Childhood remembered.

Never again will we wait
Content in the dark till our daughters
Off in the evening, somewhere,
Laughing, come home.

Robert Frost
RANGE-FINDING

The battle rent a cobweb diamond-strung
And cut a flower beside a ground bird's nest
Before it stained a single human breast.
The stricken flower bent double and so hung.
And still the bird revisited her young.
A butterfly its fall had dispossessed
A moment sought in air his flower of rest,
Then lightly stooped to it and fluttering clung.
On the bare upland pasture there had spread

O'ernight 'twixt mullein stalks a wheel of thread
And straining cables wet with silver dew.
A sudden passing bullet shook it dry.
The indwelling spider ran to greet the fly,
But finding nothing, sullenly withdrew.

James Dickey
THE JEWEL

Forgetting I am alive, the tent comes over me
Like grass, and dangling its light on a thread,
Turning the coffee-urn green
Where the boys upon camp-stools are sitting,
    Alone, in late night.

I see my coffee curving in a cup,
A blind, steeled, brimming smile
I hold up alive in my hand.
I smile back, a smile I was issued,
    Alone, in late night.

A man doubled strangely in time,
I am waiting to walk with a flashlight
Beam, as a third, weak, drifting leg
To the aircraft standing in darkness,
    Alone, in late night.

Who packs himself into a cockpit
Suspended on clod-hopping wheels,
With the moon held still in the tail-booms,
Has taken his own vow of silence,
    Alone, in late night.

Across from him, someone snaps on
The faceted lights of a cabin.
There, like the meaning of war, he sees
A strong, poor diamond of light,
   Alone, in late night.

And inside it, a man leaning forward
In a helmet, a mask of rubber,
In the balance of a great, stressed jewel
Going through his amazing procedure
   Alone, in late night.

Truly, do I live? Or shall I die, at last,
Of waiting? Why should the fear grow loud
With the years, of being the first to give in
To the matched, priceless glow of the engines,
   Alone, in late night.

   Randall Jarrell
  A PILOT FROM THE CARRIER

Strapped at the center of the blazing wheel,
His flesh ice-white against the shattered mask,
He tears at the easy clasp, his sobbing breaths
Misting the fresh blood lightening to flame,
Darkening to smoke; trapped there in pain
And fire and breathlessness, he struggles free
Into the sunlight of the upper sky—
And falls, a quiet bundle in the sky,
The miles to warmth, to air, to waking:
To the great flowering of his life, the hemisphere
That holds his dangling years. In its long slow sway

79

The world steadies and is almost still. . . .
He is alone; and hangs in knowledge
Slight, separate, estranged: a lonely eye
Reading a child's first scrawl, the carrier's wake—
The travelling milk-like circle of a miss
Beside the plant-like genius of the smoke
That shades, on the little deck, the little blaze
Toy-like as the glitter of the wing-guns,
Shining as the fragile sun-marked plane
That grows to him, rubbed silver tipped with flame.

Stephen Spender
AIR RAID ACROSS THE BAY OF PLYMOUTH

I

Above the whispering sea
And waiting rocks of black coast,
Across the bay, the searchlight beams
Swing and swing back across the sky.

      Their ends fuse in a cone of light
Held for a bright instant up
Until they break away again
Smashing that image like a cup.

II

Delicate aluminum girders
Project phantom aerial masts
Swaying crane and derrick
Above the seas' just surging deck.

III

Triangles, parallels, parallelograms,
Experiment with hypotheses
On the blackboard sky,
Seeking that X
Where the raider is met.
Two beams cross
To chalk his cross.

IV

A sound, ragged, unseen
Is pursued by swords of light.
A thud. An instant when the whole night gleams.
Gold sequins shake out of a black-silk screen.

V

Jacob ladders slant
Up to the god of war
Who, from his heaven-high car,
Unloads upon a star
A destroying star.

Round the coast, the waves
Chuckle beneath rocks.
In the fields the corn
Sways, with metallic clicks.
Man hammers nails in Man,
High on his crucifix.

Crystal Kilgore
ON WAR

Wash your hands, War.
They're dirty. You torment, you bleed, you reek of
The pains and cries of a million forgotten men.
You dance and kick and throw your head with glee. Voom!
You're not so grand—no, not at all.

Wash your hands, War.
Don't they bother you? Can you bear to look and touch
Them day after day? I could not, I would not—not if I
Were you.

I'm told that you do some good for the world. They say
You make men of mice; they say you strengthen, unite,
Arouse the cause for protection of a common right.
Maybe you do.
But you take young husbands from their wives and babies
Never to return again.
You summon the best we have to offer, promising perhaps
To soon return.
They seldom do.
You caused to be destroyed arts and wonders of centuries'
Sweat. Long, tortuous hours of creation and agony mean
Nothing to you. You tear them to whorled shreds within
The wink of an eye.

Have you a mirror, War?
Do you look into it each day? See you the once starry-
Eyed maiden whose lover you took away? See you the graying
Old mother who wrings her hands, rocks, rocks, and prays
That she may see her son in her old age? See you the

Dying babe whose eyes roll around in their sockets and
Whose tiny stomach contracts and rumbles with pangs of
Hunger? His wretched mother lies beside him. Her
Milkless breasts heave with discontent; she dies, her
Child dies. War, see you all of this?

Wash your hands, War.
Oh, how great the effort to get them clean.
Wash for eternity. Wash with all the soaps and waters
Of ages to come! You fail!
You'll never get them clean, War—no, not now, or ever
Or even after that. You'll never—your effort's
Wasted. War.

SUMMER 1965

Louis MacNeice
BROTHER FIRE

When our brother Fire was having his dog's day
Jumping the London streets with millions of tin cans
Clanking at his tail, we heard some shadow say
'Give the dog a bone'—and so we gave him ours;
Night after night we watched him slaver and crunch away
The beams of human life, the tops of topless towers.

Which gluttony of his for us was Lenten fare
Who mother-naked, suckled with sparks, were chill
Though cotted in a grille of sizzling air
Striped like a convict—black, yellow, and red;
Thus were we weaned to knowledge of the Will
That wills the natural world but wills us dead.

83

O delicate walker, babbler, dialectician Fire,
O enemy and image of ourselves,
Did we not on those mornings after the All Clear,
When you were looting shops in elemental joy
And singing as you swarmed up city block and spire,
Echo your thought in ours? 'Destroy! Destroy!'

Karl Shapiro
THE LEG

Among the iodoform, in twilight sleep,
What have I lost? he first inquires,
Peers in the middle distance where a pain,
Ghost of a nurse, hazily moves, and day,
Her blinding presence pressing in his eyes
And now his ears. They are handling him
With rubber hands. He wants to get up.

One day beside some flowers near his nose
He will be thinking, *When will I look at it?*
And pain, still in the middle distance, will reply,
At what? and he will know it's gone,
O where! and begin to tremble and cry.
He will begin to cry as a child cries
Whose puppy is mangled under a screaming wheel.

Later, as if deliberately, his fingers
Begin to explore the stump. He learns a shape
That is comfortable and tucked in like a sock.
This has a sense of humor, this can despise
The finest surgical limb, the dignity of limping,
The nonsense of wheel chairs. Now he smiles to the wall:
The amputation becomes an acquisition.

For the leg is wondering where he is (all is not lost)
And surely he had a duty to the leg;
He is its injury, the leg is his orphan,
He must cultivate the mind of the leg,
Pray for the part that is missing, pray for peace
In the image of man, pray, pray for its safety,
After a little it will die quietly.

The body, what is it, Father, but a sign
To love the force that grows us, to give back
What in Thy palm is senselessness and mud?
Knead, knead the substance of our understanding
Which must be beautiful in flesh to walk,
That if Thou take me angrily in hand
And hurl me to the shark, I shall not die!

Charles Causley
RECRUITING DRIVE

Under the willow the willow
    I heard the butcher-bird sing,
Come out you fine young fellow
    From under your mother's wing.
I'll show you the magic garden
    That hangs in the beamy air,
The way of the lynx and the angry Sphinx
    And the fun of the freezing fair.

Lie down lie down with my daughter
    Beneath the Arabian tree,
Gaze on your face in the water
    Forget the scribbling sea.

85

Your pillow the nine bright shiners
    Your bed the spilling sand,
But the terrible toy of my lily-white boy
    Is the gun in his innocent hand.

You must take off your clothes for the doctor
    And stand as straight as a pin,
His hand of stone on your white breast-bone
    Where the bullets all go in.
They'll dress you in lawn and linen
    And fill you with Plymouth gin,
O the devil may wear a rose in his hair
    I'll wear my fine doe-skin.

My mother weeps as I leave her
    But I tell her it won't be long,
The murderers wail in Wandsworth Gaol
    But I shoot a more popular song.
Down in the enemy country
    Under the enemy tree
There lies a lad whose heart has gone bad
    Waiting for me, for me.

He says I have no culture
    And that when I've stormed the pass
I shall fall on the farm with a smoking arm
    And ravish his bonny lass.
Under the willow the willow
    Death spreads her dripping wings
And caught in the snare of the bleeding air
    The butcher-bird sings, sings, sings.

Randall Jarrell
THE METAMORPHOSES

Where I spat in the harbor the oranges were bobbing
All salted and sodden, with eyes in their rinds;
The sky was all black where the coffee was burning,
And the rust of the freighters had reddened the tide.

But soon all the chimneys were burning with contracts,
The tankers rode low in the oil-black bay,
The wharves were a maze of the crated bombers,
And they gave me a job and I worked all day.

And the orders were filled; but I float in the harbor,
All tarry swollen, with gills in my sides,
The sky is all black where the carrier's burning,
And the blood of the transports is red on the tide.

James Scully
LT. CMDR. T. E. SANDERSON
15 DECEMBER 1963

None of the brass hatters had seen
the flight plan, nor what orders were,
but judged the thing to be routine.

Part shooting star, the Grumman Tracker
harrowing a suburb ·. . . It left
headlines. Looked-at hard, the picture

grows atoms, ungathering grains.
He'd come of nothing and made it
after a fashion. What remains

is what to make of him: not torn
out of a dream but living it
who took-off on Sunday, airborne

in Hingham, Mass. . . . I lie awake
mulling over my mother's note;
embossed, its plumes cap-off the wake:

"just like President Kennedy's,
the American flag on it
& closed." Not having died at ease

nor in a war, he lay in state,
the case being shut (no news leak
nor angel to uncover it)

and screwed up, sealed the way he went.
All that he was, he had become
by virtue of self government.

The thing is, what to make of it,
of the nation's arms his nation
made of him. Perhaps bit by bit

it all falls together, but then
the thing is Tommy Sanderson
my cousin, fellow citizen,

a uniform of flesh and blood
shoved back into the marshes, down
the Commonwealth, in Hingham mud.

Better to give up, than acquit;
whatever it was he meant
a whole creation weighs on it.

Keith Wilson
GUERRILLA CAMP
KOREA, 1952

We arrived at Sok To
before dawn, caught the last
of the tide & slipped the LST's bow
high on the beach.

> He was waiting, bent
> slightly over, hiding
> his hand. He didn't
> wave.

Later, after a good breakfast
aboard, an Army captain took
us on a tour of the guerrilla
camp:

> & he followed, tagged
> along like somebody's
> dog. A tall Korean,
> patient.

We were shown the kitchens, & the
tent barracks, the specially built
junks with their concealed engines

& he watched, never
leaving us with his
eyes

Through the hospital, saw 4
sheetcovered bodies from the
raid the night before, didn't
ask whose men they were, spoke
kindly to the wounded & gave
them cigarettes

until he strode up,
stuck his shattered hand
in my face, anger & hatred
flaming in his eyes &
shouted & shouted & shouted

waving that hand, the
bone crumpled by
a rifle slug & pushed
almost through the skin,
hardened into a glistening
knot

He was one of ours, a retired fighter,
about my age, my height. They told me
he wanted to know how a man
could farm
with a hand like that.

from *Graves Registry*
FOR HELOISE

TO LAY
HIS BRAIN
UPON
THE BOARD

Poems of Confession

Anne Sexton
KIND SIR: THESE WOODS

For a man needs only to be turned around once
with his eyes shut in this world to be lost. . . .
Not til we are lost . . . do we begin to find ourselves.

THOREAU, Walden

Kind Sir: This is an old game
that we played when we were eight and ten.
Sometimes on The Island, in down Maine,
in late August, when the cold fog blew in
off the ocean, the forest between Dingley Dell
and grandfather's cottage grew white and strange.
It was as if every pine tree were a brown pole
we did not know; as if day had rearranged
into night and bats flew in sun. It was a trick
to turn around once and know you were lost;
knowing the crow's horn was crying in the dark,
knowing that supper would never come, that the coasts's
cry of doom from that far away bell buoy's bell
said your nursemaid is gone. O Mademoiselle,
the rowboat rocked over. Then you were dead.
Turn around once, eyes tight, the thought in your head.

Kind Sir: Lost and of your same kind
I have turned around twice with my eyes sealed
and the woods were white and my night mind
saw such strange happenings, untold and unreal.
And opening my eyes, I am afraid of course
to look—this inward look that society scorns—
Still, I search in these woods and find nothing worse
than myself, caught between the grapes and the thorns.

93

John Hall Wheelock
THE BLACK PANTHER

There is a panther caged within my breast,
But what his name, there is no breast shall know
Save mine, nor what it is that drives him so,
Backward and forward, in relentless quest—
That silent rage, baffled but unsuppressed,
The soft pad of those stealthy feet that go
Over my body's prison to and fro,
Trying the walls forever without rest.

All day I feed him with my living heart,
But when the night puts forth her dreams and stars,
The inexorable frenzy reawakes:
His wrath is hurled upon the trembling bars,
The eternal passion stretches me apart,
And I lie silent—but my body shakes.

Donald Hall
SELF-PORTRAIT, AS A BEAR

Here is a fat animal, a bear
that is partly a dodo.
Ridiculous wings hang at his shoulders
as if they were collarbones
while he plods in the bad brickyards
at the edge of the city smiling
and eating flowers. He eats them
because he loves them
because they are beautiful
because they love him.

94

It is eating flowers which makes him fat.
He carries his huge stomach
over the gutters of damp leaves
in the parking lots in October,
but inside that paunch
he knows there are fields of lupine
and meadows of mustard and poppy.
He encloses sunshine.
Winds bend the flowers
in combers across the valley,
birds hang on the stiff wind,
at night there are showers, and the sun
lifts through a haze every morning
of the summer in the stomach.

Robert Graves
FROM THE EMBASSY

I, an ambassador of Otherwhere
To the unfederated states of Here and There
Enjoy (as the phrase is)
Extra-territorial privileges.
With heres and theres I seldom come to blows
Or need, as once, to sandbag all my windows.
And though the Otherwhereish currency
Cannot be quoted yet officially,
I meet less hindrance now with the exchange
Nor is my garb, even, considered strange;
And shy enquiries for literature
Come in by every post, and the side door.

Wendell Berry
THE GUEST

Washed into the doorway
by the wake of the traffic,
he wears humanity
like a third-hand shirt
—blackened with enough
of Manhattan's dirt to sprout
a tree, or poison one.
His empty hand has led him
where he has come to.
Our differences claim us.
He holds out his hand,
in need of all that's mine.

And so we're joined, as deep
as son and father. His life
is offered me to choose.

Shall I begin servitude
to him? Let this cup pass.
Who am I? But charity must
suppose, knowing no better,
that this is a man fallen
among thieves, or come
to this strait by no fault
—that our difference
is not a judgment,
though I can afford to eat
and am made his judge.

Robert Frost
ACQUAINTED WITH THE NIGHT

I have been one acquainted with the night.
I have walked out in rain—and back in rain.
I have outwalked the furthest city light.

I have looked down the saddest city lane.
I have passed by the watchman on his beat
And dropped my eyes, unwilling to explain.

I have stood still and stopped the sound of feet
When far away an interrupted cry
Came over houses from another street,

But not to call me back or say good-by;
And further still at an unearthly height,
One luminary clock against the sky

Proclaimed the time was neither wrong nor right.
I have been one acquainted with the night.

May Swenson
CAUSE AND EFFECT

Am I the bullet,
or the target,
or the hand
that holds the gun,
or the whisper
in the brain
saying: *Aim, Fire?*

Is the bullet innocent
though it kill?
Must the target stand
unblinking and still?
Can one escape
or the other stop
if it will?

Will the trigger-finger
obey through force?
If the hand
reverse command,
will the pregnant gun
abort its curse?

The brain,
surely it can refrain:
unclench the gun,
break open the pod
of murder,
let the target
rise and run.

First the whisper
must be caught
before the shot,
the single wasp
be burnt out:

Before the nest,
infested, swarms
to a multiple shout,
each sting
a trigger pressed.

David Ignatow
FOR ONE MOMENT

You take the dollar
and hand it to the fellow beside you
who turns and gives it to the next one
down the line. The world being round,
you stand waiting, smoking and lifting
a cup of coffee to your lips, talking
of seasonal weather and hinting
at problems. The dollar returns,
the coffee spills to the ground
in your hurry. You have the money
in one hand, a cup in the other,
a cigarette in your mouth,
and for one moment have forgotten
what it is you have to do,
your hair grey, your legs weakened
from long standing.

Sylvia Plath
THE ARRIVAL OF THE BEE BOX

I ordered this, this clean wood box
Square as a chair and almost too heavy to lift.
I would say it was the coffin of a midget
Or a square baby
Were there not such a din in it.

The box is locked, it is dangerous.
I have to live with it overnight
And I can't keep away from it.

There are no windows, so I can't see what is in there.
There is only a little grid, no exit.

I put my eye to the grid.
It is dark, dark,
With the swarmy feeling of African hands
Minute and shrunk for export,
Black on black, angrily clambering.

How can I let them out?
It is the noise that appals me most of all,
The unintelligible syllables.
It is like a Roman mob.
Small, taken one by one, but my god, together!

I lay my ear to furious Latin.
I am not a Caesar.
I have simply ordered a box of maniacs.
They can be sent back.
They can die, I need feed them nothing. I am the owner.

I wonder how hungry they are.
I wonder if they would forget me
If I just undid the locks and stood back and turned into a tree.
There is the laburnum, its blond colonnades,
And the petticoats of the cherry.

They might ignore me immediately
In my moon suit and funeral veil.
I am no source of honey
So why should they turn on me?
Tomorrow I will be sweet God, I will set them free.

The box is only temporary.

Langston Hughes
AS I GREW OLDER

It was a long time ago.
I have almost forgotten my dream.
But it was there then,
In front of me,
Bright like a sun—
My dream.

And then the wall rose,
Rose slowly,
Slowly,
Between me and my dream.
Rose slowly, slowly,
Dimming,
Hiding,
The light of my dream.
Rose until it touched the sky—
The wall.

Shadow.
I am black.

I lie down in the shadow.
No longer the light of my dream before me,
Above me.
Only the thick wall.
Only the shadow.

My hands!
My dark hands!
Break through the wall!

Find my dream!
Help me to shatter this darkness,
To smash this night,
To break this shadow
Into a thousand lights of sun,
Into a thousand whirling dreams
Of sun!

James Dickey
ENCOUNTER IN THE CAGE
COUNTRY

What I was would not work
For them all, for I had not caught
The lion's eye. I was walking down

The cellblock in green glasses   and came
At last to the place where someone was hiding
His spots in his black hide.

Unchangeably they were there,
Driven in as by eyes
Like mine, his darkness ablaze

In the stinking sun of the beast house.
Among the crowd, he found me
Out   and dropped his bloody snack

And came to the perilous edge
Of the cage, where the great bars tremble
Like wire. All Sunday ambling stopped,

The curved cells tightened around
Us all   as we saw he was watching only
Me. I knew the stage was set, and I began

To perform   first saunt'ring   then stalking
Back and forth like a sentry   faked
As if to run   and at one brilliant move

I made as though drawing a gun from my hip-
bone, the bite-sized children broke
Up   changing their concept of laughter,

But none of this changed his eyes, or changed
My green glasses. Alert, attentive,
He waited for what I could give him:

My moves   my throat   my wildest love,
The eyes behind my eyes. Instead, I left
Him, though he followed me right to the end

Of concrete. I wiped my face, and lifted off
My glasses. Light blasted the world of shade
Back under every park bush   the crowd

Quailed from me   I was inside and out
Of myself   and something was given a life-
mission to say to me hungrily over

And over and over   *your moves are exactly right*
For a few things in this world: we know you
When you come, Green Eyes, Green Eyes.

Lisel Mueller
NAMES

A few names tell it all,
the whole incredible history
of one generation, mine;
names that we cannot manage
with a drum-roll, like Waterloo,
nor pitch to the eloquence
of tragic Gettysburg.

Hiroshima sticks in our throats;
We choke on the bones of Buchenwald,
spit out the stones of Berlin.
     Who says Vietnam
     burns his tongue,
and Mississippi, o Mississippi
scrubs out our mouths
till we cry mercy.

Jon Stallworthy
FIRST BLOOD

It was. The breach smelling of oil,
The stock of resin—buried snug
In the shoulder. Not too much recoil
At the firing of the first slug

(Jubilantly into the air)
Nor yet too little. Targets pinned
Against a tree: shot down: and there
Abandoned to the sniping wind.

My turn first to carry the gun.
Indian file and camouflaged
With contours of green shade and sun
We ghosted between larch and larch.

A movement between branches—thump
Of a fallen cone. The barrel
Jumps, making branches jump
Higher, dislodging the squirrel

To the next tree. Your turn, my turn.
The silhouette retracts its head.
A hit. 'Let's go back to the lawn.'
'We can't leave it carrying lead

For the rest of its life. Reload.
Finish him off. Reload again.'
It was now *him*, and when he showed
The sky cracked like a window pane.

He broke away: traversed a full
Half dozen trees: vanished. Had found
A hole? We watched that terrible
Slow spiral to the clubbing ground.

His back was to the tree. His eyes
Were gun barrels. He was dumb,
And we could not see past the size
Of his hands or hear for the drum

In his side. Four shots point-blank
To dull his eyes, a fifth to stop
The shiver in his clotted flank.
A fling of earth. As we stood up

The larches closed their ranks. And when
Earth would not muffle the drumming blood
We, like dishonoured soldiers, ran
the gauntlet of a darkening wood.

Vassar Miller
RESOLVE

I must go back to the small place,
to the swept place,
to the still place,
to the silence under the drip of the dew,
under the beat of the bird's pulse,
under the whir of the gnat's wing,
to the silence under the absence of noise,
there bathe my hands and my heart
in the hush,
there rinse my ears and my eyes,
there know Thy voice and Thy face,
until when, O my God, do I knock
with motionless knuckles
on the crystal door of the air
hung on the hinge of the wind.

William H. Matchett
MIDDLE-MAN

I guess my political point of view
Is something akin to a riddle,
Though I hadn't imagined there were so few
Who stood, like myself, in the middle.

No one trusts me in tracing trends
Or noting the natures of nations;
I'm considered conservative by my friends
And radical by my relations.

When the talk gets around to discussing me—
And it does before too long—
My friends and relations all agree
On one point, which is that I'm wrong.

I'm a bourgeois bum, or a dirty red,
The Lord knows what I'm seeking;
I've a long way to go, or I've lost my head,
Depending on who is speaking.

And so before any discussion ends
I've been damned by both congregations,
As a hopeless conservative by my friends
And a radical by my relations.

Robert Creeley
INTERVALS

Who
am I—
identity
singing.

Place
a lake
on ground, water
finds a form.

Smoke
on the air
goes higher
to fade.

Sun bright,
trees dark green,
a little movement
in the leaves.

Birds singing
measure distance,
intervals between
echo silence.

Wallace Stevens
DOMINATION OF BLACK

At night, by the fire,
The colors of the bushes
And of the fallen leaves,
Repeating themselves,
Turned in the room,
Like the leaves themselves
Turning in the wind.
Yes: but the color of the heavy hemlocks
Came striding.
And I remembered the cry of the peacocks.

The colors of their tails
Were like the leaves themselves
Turning in the wind,

In the twilight wind.
They swept over the room,
Just as they flew from the boughs of the
    hemlocks
Down to the ground.
I heard them cry—the peacocks.
Was it a cry against the twilight
Or against the leaves themselves
Turning in the wind,
Turning as the flames
Turned in the fire,
Turning as the tails of the peacocks
Turned in the loud fire,
Loud as the hemlocks
Full of the cry of the peacocks?
Or was it a cry against the hemlocks?

Out of the window,
I saw how the planets gathered
Like the leaves themselves
Turning in the wind.
I saw how the night came,
Came striding like the color of the heavy
    hemlocks
I felt afraid.
And I remembered the cry of the peacocks.

Shirley Bridges
IMAGINARY FIGURES OF THE VIRTUES

FAITH BY ROY LICHTENSTEIN

In the street, when they march by in short—
      Or long-haired uniform,
      Carrying guns/placards/bouquets
      Shouting freedom/peace/fraternity
She stands aside;
When they ask, Don't you live to die for a cause?
She says
No.

In a church, when all the other girls
      Blush behind yards of veiling
      And rustle into servitude
      At the tinkle of a bell,
She peeps behind a pillar;
When they ask, Don't you adore the chaste
          Mysteries of the god?
She says
No.

At a party, when they hand round
      Reefers and hearts, needle
      The heirs of Cupid and Bacchus,
She holds a glass of water;
When they ask, Hi kid, aren't you hip,
      Don't you care for kicks?
She says
No.

At a meeting, when they discuss hormones
       And broilers and compost,
       The descant of nature,
She leans against an Oxfam poster;
When they ask, Don't you think we should
       Prohibit the use of all chemical
       Pesticides and fertilizers?
She says
No.

In the stretch of her skin, while they cover the pages
       With eye-strain and scribble
       To support a thesis,
She lies in the middle of a field;
    You're not like us,
    The lark's rhetoric bubbles,
    Are you?
No, she says,
No;
I dance with the living
And watch with the dying
And to all truth's PR men
Say
No.

BEYOND
THE COMPASS
OF CHANGE
The Wonders of Life and Death

Robert Creeley
THE RHYTHM

It is all a rhythm,
from the shutting
door, to the window
opening,

the seasons, the sun's
light, the moon,
the oceans, the
growing of things,

the mind in men
personal, recurring
in them again,
thinking the end

is not the end, the
time returning,
themselves dead but
someone else coming.

If in death I am dead,
then in life also
dying, dying . . .
And the women cry and die.

The little children
grow only to old men.
The grass dries,
the force goes.

But is met by another
returning, oh not mine,
not mine, and
in turn dies.

The rhythm which projects
from itself continuity
bending all to its force
from window to door,
from ceiling to floor,
light at the opening
dark at the closing.

Gwendolyn Brooks
the birth in a narrow room

Weeps out of western country something new.
Blurred and stupendous. Wanted and unplanned.
     Winks. Twines, and weakly winks
Upon the milk-glass fruit bowl, iron pot,
The bashful china child tipping forever
Yellow apron and spilling pretty cherries.

Now, weeks and years will go before she thinks
"How pinchy is my room! how can I breathe!
I am not anything and I have got
Not anything, or anything to do!"—
But prances nevertheless with gods and fairies
Blithely about the pump and then beneath
The elms and grapevines, then in darling endeavor
By privy foyer, where the screenings stand
And where the bugs buzz by in private cars
Across old peach cans and old jelly jars.

Lisel Mueller
CIVILIZING THE CHILD

You can't keep it, I say,
it will decay.
Bury the mouse, I tell her,
it will make the tulips redder,
give the trees babies,
fatten the faces of daisies,
put manes on the grass.
Spring comes up thick from the dead, I say,
broadcasting words like seeds
until she obeys, sadly,
with her green child's trowel,
And when she runs out the next morning
to see if the pink hawthorn
has an extra blossom or two
—and it has, it has!—
I go scot-free, acquitted
by her happiness-tinged cheeks,
my judges, my blind jury.

Ann Stanford
THE RIDERS
FOR EUNICE

We made castles of grass, green halls, enormous stem-lined
rooms
And sailed in trees.
Close to the backyard fence
We dug a cave.
We never finished it,

But there was plenty of time for moving that last foot or two
    of earth,
It was an eternity till Christmas.

Do you remember the yellow fields
We tussled through, small mustard petals clinging?
And the hikes on Saturday up to the grove of oaks?
Plenty of time then, and dark came down before we were
home.
They were out calling and searching.

There was a winter year and a summer year.
The last was for beaches.
Salt wind over the gaudy pier,
And things moved faster.
You on the yellow horse, I on the dun.
One way the sea, the battleship,
The pier, the fishers leaning by the rail,
The ferris wheel,
And turning still
The shoddy mermaid painted on the wall.
Up and down we laughed and caught the rings.
And one was gold for summer.

Then summer was gone, and the horse bunched warm ripples
Trotting through orchards down to the practice ring.
His eyes were like suns, when he changed his gait
Faster and faster till the trees blurred and the sky
And there were only posts and the wind and the packed earth
And the warm beast gathering and springing.
How to get off, how to escape!
At last I fell, but it was no better.

The earth turned under my back
Swift, swift, we turned out of day to night to day again,
Light and shadow from a picket fence.

And the planet whirled on the sun, a swift carousel.

Our heads grow gray, our children laugh in the long grasses.

Adrienne Rich
BEARS

Wonderful bears that walked my room all night,
Where are you gone, your sleek and fairy fur,
Your eyes' veiled imperious light?

Brown bears as rich as mocha or as musk,
White opalescent bears whose fur stood out
Electric in the deepening dusk,

And great black bears who seemed more blue than black,
More violet than blue against the dark—
Where are you now? upon what track

Mutter your muffled paws, that used to tread
So softly, surely, up the creakless stair
While I lay listening in bed?

When did I lose you? whose have you become?
Why do I wait and wait and never hear
Your thick nocturnal pacing in my room?
My bears, who keeps you now, in pride and fear?

Galway Kinnell
FIRST SONG

Then it was dusk in Illinois, the small boy
After an afternoon of carting dung
Hung on the rail fence, a sapped thing
Weary to crying. Dark was growing tall
And he began to hear the pond frogs all
Calling on his ear with what seemed their joy.

Soon their sound was pleasant for a boy
Listening in the smoky dusk and the nightfall
Of Illinois, and from the fields two small
Boys came bearing cornstalk violins
And they rubbed the cornstalk bows with resins
And the three sat there scraping of their joy.

It was now fine music the frogs and the boys
Did in the towering Illinois twilight make
And into dark in spite of a shoulder's ache
A boy's hunched body loved out of a stalk
The first song of his happiness, and the song woke
His heart to the darkness and into the sadness of joy.

Jon Stallworthy
OUT OF BOUNDS

The world was flat, lawn without end,
When first we left the house. Later we stood
At the world's edge over a newfound land
Dizzy with orchards. These and the tall wood
Contained us for six summers: meadow and

Wilderness a seventh. Then we found
The fence that proved the world was round.

We broke out over the dead
Limb of a larch and in the Colonel's park
Trespassed till supper, trespassed all that year.
Emerging once from the wood's cathedral dark
We saw miles off, but every sail-rib clear,
A windmill standing at ease, its head
Laurelled with small, bright clouds. We said,

'We could do it in half a day.'
The sun was in mid flight. Down the first hill
Bracken stampeded with us, cantered up
The second, ambled up the third. The mill
Like a schooner from wave top to wave top
Whenever we closed seemed to veer away:
Nautical miles between us lay.

Minute by minute the sun burned
Down like a rick into red ash, fading
To grey, then charcoal. We were gaining now
On a giant in seven-league boots, wading
Thigh-deep, head-down, over seas of plough

And plunging grass, who as we looked lurched, turned
Back: and the darkness churned.

Like skeletal arms the black
Sweeps gestured to the sky. One field to cross;
Another to go round; a stile; we went
Stumbling between tall hedges, and there was
One field more. As if by common consent,

With hardly a word spoken, we turned back
Shoulder to shoulder down the track.

Afterwards we said, 'Another time
We will start earlier,' but though we went
Many fields further, north, south, east and west
Of the windmill, by that same consent
We left it undisturbed. Though I have crossed
Mountains and seas since, I have yet to climb
A hill not seven miles from home.

To climb for what? To find a grey
Skull, lickened, cobweb-raftered, with the wind
A ghost lamenting through its broken teeth?
Better to leave the features undefined
Than rob the landscape of a last wild myth.
Still the sweeps signal in my head: are they
Beckoning, or waving us away?

Jack Mathews
THE CATFISH

I spent afternoons like an old man's drowsy years,
fishing the creek water, as frothed and gold as lager,
catching river cats beyond the ironwood spears.
But with every catch, I hoped there was another, bigger.

And began to think there was a king of catfish there,
inert as a sack of coins in the bottom mud, wise
as he meditated in his dream-dark lair,
from a tarbucket head and two pale green eyes.

From a study of the specimens expiring on the bank,
I formed a picture of the mammoth one: grumpy, old,
heavy as a tub of cheese, uncleansed by water, rank.
He oared himself erect inside my mind and glowed.

His skin was twisted like a woman's hose upon his sides,
his mouth was tasseled like a lamp with ancient hooks;
now this embodied silence simply lasts beneath the tides
as remote from baits and lures as from the flight of ducks.

I've thought upon my monster beyond the range
of credulity; accepted him as if he really existed
and shook the abutments of my reason. Beyond change,
in a myth beyond begetting, this thing has lasted.

The real ones, I have found, are mortal in the mind
as in the world of hooks and worms and lethal boys.
The dreamed one lasts on where he's never been,
untroubled as a star by hooks and facts and other toys.

Joseph Langland
SACRIFICE OF A RAINBOW TROUT

Suddenly, from the rocky spring
A trout hung, trembling, in the air,
A jewel to the morning sun;

And then upon the mossy banks,
Rainy with rainbows, up he leaped
And tumbled wildly in the grass.

123

I ran to catch him where my hook
Pinned him behind a crusted rock
And ripped his mouth and gills apart.

I pulled his foaming stomach clean
And washed my fingers in the spring
And sat down and admired him.

His sunlit scales upon my hands,
I wrapped his flesh in leaves of elm
And homeward, singing, carried him.

I stripped him of his ivory bones,
Then held him, shining, to the fire
And tongued his body to my own.

And that was the supper that I had
While my imagination fed
Its silver hook upon the world.

Lawrence Hetrick
ARROWHEAD FIELD

Down from a drummed steel highway
I drive under shade trees, and I am
Home for musty August once again.

Nothing's doing, nothing's new
In the depths of sleeping green.
Those who live here are away.

Dizzy with floating, puddled glare,
I pass familiar turns, aimlessly roll
To forms of cropless sand, and stop.

I wade in a crumbling uphill field
Where my father led me to find
Arrowheads, substantial flakes of light.

Here they lie, beneath mirages,
Sinking farther out of sight.
No wind, no moon, no cloud is here.

Where can I be except this place
Whispering to me in every grain?
My shadow swings down from my feet.

The light plunges into burning fields
That all alike roll away and arch
From town to town, over the earth.

Robert Pack
THE BOAT

I dressed my father in his little clothes,
Blue sailor suit, brass buttons on his coat.
He asked me where the running water goes.

"Down to the sea," I said; "Set it afloat!"
Beside the stream he bent and raised the sail,
Uncurled the string and launched the painted boat.

White birds, flown like flags, wrenched his eyes pale.
He leaped on the tight deck and took the wind.
I watched the ship foam lurching in the gale,

And cried, "Come back, you don't know what you'll find!"
He steered. The ship grew, reddening the sky.
Water throbbed backward, blind stumbling after blind.

The rusty storm diminished in his eye,
And down he looked at me. A harbor rose.
I asked, "What happens, father, when you die?"

He told me where all the running water goes,
And dressed me gently in my little clothes.

William H. Matchett
AUNT ALICE IN APRIL

By mid-day it was warm enough; she climbed
The path up through the orchard, stopping twice
To catch her breath and give her heart a rest.
Just to the left there somewhere, past the rock
Shaped like a sugar-loaf, the child had found
The bloodroot blooming and had stained her hands.

It was no use; her eyesight was too weak.
She could not find them and she dared not kneel
With no one there to help her up. She sighed
And peered around her at the feathering leaves.

Yes, it was truly spring once more.
                                    She turned
And made her slow way back down to the house.

Ann Stanford

AN ANNIVERSARY: A COUNTRY BURIAL

Again December shadowed and gray—
A time to die for one who lived by sun—
Brings unshaped mornings, set behind clouds
And takes remembrance a year away.

And still I ride in hushed December sound
Past fields long gathered, and the stubble thin,
To the iron gates, and turn beside the grass—
The road is gravel then—to the fresh mound.

Odd how the shaft of light for an hour shone
(Though the day was rain before and afterward)
Across the pile of bloom, the orchard rows,
The restlessness of mourners gazing on.

We talked and went away, the flowers there
Sweetened the air of many afternoons
In an empty place, where none but loss shall come
With a greeting whispered, foolish, in the air.

May Swenson
DEATH
GREAT SMOOTHENER

Death
great smoothener
maker of order
arrester unraveler sifter and changer
death great hoarder
student stranger drifter traveler
flyer and nester all caught at your border
death
great halter
blackener and frightener
reducer dissolver
seizer and welder of younger with elder
waker with sleeper
death great keeper
of all that must alter
death
great heightener
leaper evolver
great smoothener
great whitener

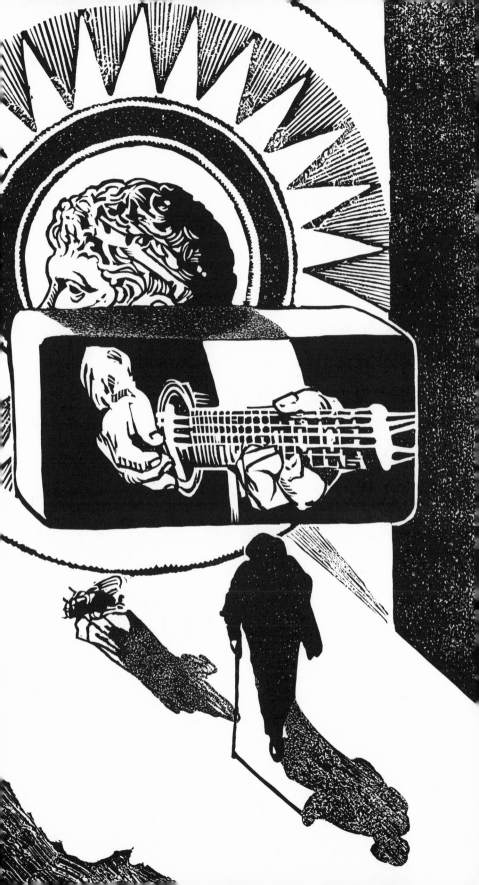

PERCEIVED IN A FINAL ATMOSPHERE

Reflections on the Human Condition

May Swenson
THE UNIVERSE

What
is it about,
the universe
about
us stretching out? We within our brains within it think
we must unspin the laws that spin it. We think
why because
we think
because.
Because
we think
we think
the universe
about
us.
But does it think,
the universe?
Then what
about?
About
us? If not, must there be cause
in the universe?
Must it have laws? And what
if the universe
is *not about*
us? Then what?
What
is it about
and what
about
us?

Denise Levertov
A MAN

'Living a life'—
the beauty of deep lines
dug in your cheeks.

The years gather by sevens
to fashion you. They are blind,
but you are not blind.

Their blows resound,
they are deaf, those laboring
daughters of the Fates,

but you are not deaf,
you pick out
your own song from the uproar

line by line,
and at last throw back
your head and sing it.

Jack Kerouac
121ST CHORUS

Everything is in the same moment
It doesn't matter how much money you have
It's happening feebly now,
        the works
I can taste the uneaten food
        I'll find

132

In the next city
    in this dream

I can feel the iron railroads
    like marshmallow

I can't tell the difference
    between mental and real

It's all happening
It won't end
It'll be good
The money that was to have been spent
   on the backward nations
of the world, has already been
   spent in Forward Time

Forward to the Sea,
   and the Sea Comes back to you
   and there's no escaping
   when you're a fish
   the nets of summer destiny

    Horace Gregory
    SPYGLASS

This a spyglass: it
Reads the deepest waters,
Reads the weather, it tells
The time of day, it pierces
Fog and cloud, it searches out
The moon, the sun; it is

133

A lidless eye, open at morning
And alive at night.

Touch it: even blind senses
Know its ceaseless stare,
How it looks inward to
The dark and how it gazes
Through the outer air

It is
The spyglass: it is now
Directed across the plain,
Over a broken bridge, into
The forest, through elm and pine,
Oak leaf and briar, a side of
Rock, a glint of water, the ivy
Vine—careful, the glass is very
Powerful, one can scarcely
Hold it—it has seen
Something that moves, that runs,
Throws itself flat,
Leaps, circles as it shot,
Stands upright, dives, yet cannot
Escape the glass. It is
Running, it has tripped, is
Running, it has grown smaller
Than its shadow, it has lost
Its shadow among the branches,
Among the leaves. The glass
Has caught its face; it is
What we thought it was, not quite
An animal—its pelt is fluttering
In rags—not quite a god;

It is not hard to know what
Its strange features mean;
It falls again; it is
The disappearing man.

Robert Lowell
FALL 1961

Back and forth, back and forth
goes the tock, tock, tock
of the orange, bland, ambassadorial
face of the moon
on the grandfather clock.

All autumn, the chafe and jar
of nuclear war;
we have talked our extinction to death.
I swim like a minnow
behind my studio window.

Our end drifts nearer,
the moon lifts,
radiant with terror.
The state
is a diver under a glass bell.

A father's no shield
for his child.
We are like a lot of wild
spiders crying together,
but without tears.

Nature holds up a mirror.
One swallow makes a summer.
It's easy to tick
off the minutes,
but the clockhands stick.

Back and forth!
Back and forth, back and forth—
my one point of rest
is the orange and black
oriole's swinging nest!

William Stafford
A STARED STORY

Over the hill came horsemen, horsemen whistling.
They were all hard-driven, stamp, stamp, stamp.
Legs withdrawn and delivered again like pistons,
down they rode into the winter camp,
and while earth whirled on its forgotten center
these travelers feasted till dark in the lodge of their chief.
Into the night at last on earth their mother
they drummed away; the farthest hoofbeat ceased.

Often at cutbanks where roots hold dirt together
survivors pause in the sunlight, quiet, pretending
that stared story—and gazing at earth their mother:
all journey far, hearts beating, to some such ending.
And all, slung here in our cynical constellation,
whistle the wild world, live by imagination.

W. H. Auden
LEAP BEFORE YOU LOOK

The sense of danger must not disappear:
The way is certainly both short and steep,
However gradual it looks from here;
Look if you like, but you will have to leap.

Tough-minded men get mushy in their sleep
And break the by-laws any fool can keep;
It is not the convention but the fear
That has a tendency to disappear.

The worried efforts of the busy heap,
The dirt, the imprecision, and the beer
Produce a few smart wisecracks every year;
Laugh if you can, but you will have to leap.

The clothes that are considered right to wear
Will not be either sensible or cheap,
So long as we consent to live like sheep
And never mention those who disappear.

Much can be said for social savoir-faire,
But to rejoice when no one else is there
Is even harder than it is to weep;
No one is watching, but you have to leap.

A solitude ten thousand fathoms deep
Sustains the bed on which we lie, my dear:
Although I love you, you will have to leap;
Our dream of safety has to disappear.

William Meredith
THE FEAR OF BEASTS

Pity the nightly tiger: fierce and wise,
He works upwind; the moonlight stripes his glade;
No one could hear that tread,
Least of all his guileless, watering prize.
And yet, the wonder is, he is afraid.
At the water-hole, one look from dreaming eyes,
From sleeping throat the feeblest of cries,
Will prove ambush enough to strike him dead.
A beast in a human dream must go in dread
Of the chance awakening on which he dies.

Robert Graves
NOBODY

Nobody, ancient mischief, nobody,
Harasses always with an absent body.

Nobody coming up the road, nobody,
Like a tall man in a dark cloak, nobody.

Nobody about the house, nobody,
Like children creeping up the stairs, nobody.

Nobody anywhere in the garden, nobody,
Like a young girl quiet with needlework, nobody.

Nobody coming, nobody, not yet here,
Incessantly welcomed by the wakeful ear.

Until this nobody shall consent to die
Under his curse must everybody lie—

The curse of his envy, of his grief and fright,
Of sudden rape and murder screamed in the night.

Carl Sandburg
THE LONG SHADOW OF LINCOLN:
A LITANY

(We can succeed only by concert . . . The dogmas of the
quiet past are inadequate to the stormy present. The occasion is piled high with difficulty, and we must rise with the
occasion. As our case is new so we must think anew and act
anew. We must disenthrall ourselves. . . . December 1,
1862. The President's Message to Congress.)

Be sad, be cool, be kind,
remembering those now dreamdust
hallowed in the ruts and gullies,
solemn bones under the smooth blue sea,
faces warblown in a falling rain.

Be a brother, if so can be,
to those beyond battle fatigue
each in his own corner of earth
 or forty fathoms undersea
 beyond all boom of guns,
 beyond any bong of a great bell,
 each with a bosom and number,
 each with a pack of secrets,

each with a personal dream and doorway
and over them now the long endless winds
    with the low healing song of time,
    the hush and sleep murmur of time.

Make your wit a guard and cover.
Sing low, sing high, sing wide.
Let your laughter come free
remembering looking toward peace:
"We must disenthrall ourselves."

Be a brother, if so can be,
to those thrown forward
for taking hardwon lines,
for holding hardwon points
    and their reward so-so,
little they care to talk about,
their pay held in a mute calm,
highspot memories going unspoken,
what they did being past words,
what they took being hardwon.
    Be sad, be kind, be cool.
      Weep if you must
    And weep open and shameless
      before these altars.

There are wounds past words.
There are cripples less broken
than many who walk whole.
    There are dead youths
    with wrists of silence
    who keep a vast music
    under their shut lips,

what they did being past words,
their dreams like their deaths
beyond any smooth and easy telling,
having given till no more to give.

There is dust alive
with dreams of The Republic,
with dreams of the Family of Man
flung wide on a shrinking globe
    with old timetables,
    old maps, old guide-posts
    torn into shreds,
    shot into tatters,
    burnt in a firewind,
    lost in the shambles,
    faded in rubble and ashes.

There is dust alive.
Out of a granite tomb,
Out of a bronze sarcophagus,
Loose from the stone and copper
Steps a whitesmoke ghost
Lifting an authoritative hand
In the name of dreams worth dying for,
In the name of men whose dust breathes
    of those dreams so worth dying for,
what they did being past words,
beyond all smooth and easy telling.

Be sad, be kind, be cool,
remembering under God, a dreamdust
hallowed in the ruts and gullies,
solemn bones under the smooth blue sea,
faces warblown in a falling rain.

Sing low, sing high, sing wide.
Make your wit a guard and cover.
Let your laughter come free
like a help and a brace of comfort.

The earth laughs, the sun laughs
over every wise harvest of man,
over man looking toward peace
by the light of the hard old teaching:
"We must disenthrall ourselves."

e.e. cummings
dive for dreams

dive for dreams
or a slogan may topple you
(trees are their roots
and wind is wind)

trust your heart
if the seas catch fire
(and live by love
though the stars walk backward)

honour the past
but welcome the future
(and dance your death
away at this wedding)

never mind a world
with its villains or heroes
(for god likes girls
and tomorrow and the earth)

Marianne Moore
WHAT ARE YEARS?

What is our innocence,
what is our guilt? All are
    naked, none is safe. And whence
is courage: the unanswered question,
the resolute doubt—
dumbly calling, deafly listening—that
is misfortune, even death,
    encourages others
    and in its defeat, stirs

    the soul to be strong? He
sees deep and is glad, who
    accedes to mortality
and in his imprisonment rises
upon himself as
the sea in a chasm, struggling to be
free and unable to be,
    in its surrendering
    finds it continuing.

So he who strongly feels,
behaves. The very bird,
    grown taller as he sings, steels
his form straight up. Though he is captive,
his mighty singing
says, satisfaction is a lowly
thing, how pure a thing is joy.
    This is mortality,
    this is eternity.

NOTES ON THE POETS

AUDEN, W. H.   *Leap Before You Look*

WYSTAN HUGH AUDEN was born in York, England in 1907 and educated at Oxford where he formed with C. Day Lewis, Louis MacNeice, and Stephen Spender a group of poets and social critics. In the 1930's, Auden and Christopher Isherwood combined their satirical talents to write *The Dog Beneath the Skin* (1935) and *The Ascent of F6* (1937). His poem, *Spain*, winner of the King's Medal for Poetry, sprang from his experience as a stretcher bearer during the Spanish Civil War. In 1939 he left England for the United States and in 1946 became a citizen. Auden's books of poetry and honors are numerous including: *The Age of Anxiety*, winner of the 1948 Pulitzer Prize; *Nones*, the Bollingen Prize for 1952; *The Shield of Achilles*, the 1956 National Book Award; *Homage to Clio* (1960); *About the House* (1965); *Orators* (1967); and *Collected Longer Poems* (1969). His honors abroad include a teaching fellowship from 1956 to 1962 at Oxford and the Guinness Poetry Award in 1959. Not confining himself to poetry alone, he has translated with Chester Kallman the libretto of Mozart's *The Magic Flute* and written the librettos for Igor Stravinsky's *The Rake's Progress* and Hans Werne Henze's *Elegy for Young Lovers*. Auden has also compiled several anthologies, notably the five volume *Poets of the English Language* (1952) with Norman Holmes Pearson. In 1964 he and Leif Sjoberg translated *Markings* by the late Dag Hammarskjöld. He is a member of the Academy of Arts and Letters and is Honorary President of Associate Societies of Edinburgh.

BERRY, WENDELL   *The Guest*

WENDELL BERRY was born in Louisville, Kentucky in 1934. He received both an A.B. and M.A. degree from the University of Kentucky, where he is now a member of the English Department. Previously he taught at Stanford and New York University. Wendell Berry has published two novels, *Nathan Coulter* in 1960 and *A Place on Earth* in 1964. His first book of poetry *The Broken Ground* was published in 1964 and his second, *Openings* in 1968. With his wife and two children Wendell Berry lives on a farm in Port Royal, Kentucky.

BLY, ROBERT   *Watching Television*

ROBERT BLY was born in Madison, Minnesota, in 1926. He spent two years in the Navy at the end of World War II and graduated from Harvard College in 1950. His poetic career has at least three facets: translator, creator, and political activist. In 1958 he founded *The Fifties*, a poetry magazine designed to introduce American readers to European and South American poets in both the original and in translation. *The Fifties* has, of course, now become *The Sixties* and will soon become *The Seventies*. His first book of poetry *Silence in the Snowy Fields* was published in 1962. His second volume of poems, *The Light Around the Body*, was published in 1967 and was subsequently awarded the National Book Award. Robert Bly is one of the few poets of his generation who does not teach. He now lives on a farm in western Minnesota and earns his livelihood from his poems, translations and readings.

BOOTH, PHILIP   *Choosing a Homesite*

PHILIP BOOTH was born and brought up in Hanover, New Hampshire and in Maine. He continues his close association with rural New England by spending a part of each year in Castine, Maine. After serving in the Air Force, he received a B.A. from Dartmouth and an M.A. from Columbia. He has taught at Bowdoin, Dartmouth, and Wellesley, and is currently Professor of English at Syracuse. His first book of verse, *Letter from a Distant Land*, was awarded the 1957 Lamont Prize of the Academy of American Poets. A second volume, *The Islanders*, was published in 1961 and a third, *Weathers and Edges*, in 1966. He also has the distinction of having twice been awarded a Guggenheim Fellowship.

BRIDGES, SHIRLEY   *Imaginary Figures of the Virtues*
                              Faith by Roy Lichtenstein

SHIRLEY BRIDGES was born in 1924 in London, England, where she spent her childhood. Her grandfather was Robert Bridges, former poet laureate of England. Shirley Bridges studied history for some years, including three in Italy, and taught until her marriage to the poet Hilary Corke. She and her husband live in Abinger Hammer in Surrey, England.

BROOKS, GWENDOLYN   *We Real Cool*
                                                          Jack
                                    the birth in a narrow room
          The parents: people like our marriage Maxie and Andrew

GWENDOLYN BROOKS occupies a unique place among contemporary American poets. Born in Topeka, Kansas, and growing up
in a Chicago slum, her formal education ended with graduation
from Wilson Junior College in 1936. Her first poem was published at the age of thirteen. Since then she has published a number of books of poetry including *A Street in Bronzeville* (1945),
Annie Allen (1949), *Bronzeville Boys and Girls* (1956), *Selected Poems* (1963) and *In the Mecca* (1968). She has also
written a novel, *Maud Martha*. Winner of the Pulitzer Prize, and
the recipient of two Guggenheim Fellowships, she succeeded
Carl Sandburg as poet laureate of Illinois. She had this to say of
writing commemorative poetry in her new post: "A poet is a
wild, free thing whose poems don't happen like that. I don't plan
to produce poems for special occasions." She and her husband
now live in Chicago, the scene of her latest book of poems.

CAUSLEY, CHARLES   *Recruiting Drive*

CHARLES CAUSLEY was born in Launceston, Cornwall, England in
1916. During World War II he served with the Royal Navy in
both the Mediterranean and the Pacific. After the war he finished
his studies at St. Peter's College in England. His books of poetry
include *Survivor's Leave* (1953), *Recruiting Drive* (1958), and
Johnny Alleluia (1962). He has also compiled several anthologies: *Dawn and Dusk: Poems of Our Times* (1963), and *Modern Ballads and Story Poems* (1965), published a book of short
stories, *Farewell, Aggie Weston* (1951), and written for a number of British periodicals. He is currently teaching in England.

CREELEY, ROBERT   *Intervals*
                                                     The Rhythm

ROBERT CREELEY was born in Arlington, Massachusetts in 1928.
He studied at both Harvard and Black Mountain College and
received an M.A. from the University of New Mexico. His first
book of poetry, *For Love*, was a contender for the 1962 National Book Award. His second book, *Words*, was published in
1967. In addition, he has also written a novel, *The Island*, and a

book of short stories, *The Gold Diggers*. He has been awarded
a Rockefeller Foundation grant, a Guggenheim Fellowship, and
a fellowship from the University of New Mexico. He has taught
at both the University of New Mexico and at the State University of New York at Buffalo.

cummings, e. e.   *so shy shy shy*
                                                   dive for dreams

e. e. cummings was born in Cambridge, Massachusetts in 1894.
A specialist in the Classics, he received his M.A. from Harvard
in 1916 and immediately joined an ambulance corps in North
Africa. In a typical display of defiance, he refused to claim
hatred for the Germans; instead, he said he loved the French.
The French, baffled by such a distinction of loyalty, put him
into prison as a spy. This experience provided the material for
his first book, *The Enormous Room* (1922). In spite of his ordeal, he chose Paris as his home after the war. There he turned
most of his attention to painting. Eventually, he returned to the
United States where he proved himself to be an extremely innovative poet, illustrator of his own poems, writer of three plays
and one ballet, and a critic of literature and art. His knowledge
of the intricacies of classical Greek made him realize the limitations of the English language. His novel phrasing and disdain for
accepted word structure and punctuation was an attempt to
make English a more flexible language. Of the difference between his clear simple drawings and complex verse, he said: "I
have no sentimental fear of sentimentality. There's great pressure on soft people today to try to be hard. Since my writing is
hard, then the natural thing would be that my paintings are soft."
His book of poems include *one times one* (1954), *95 poems*
(1958), *one hundred selected poems* (1959) and *fifty poems*
(1960). Before his death in 1962 he received many honors including a special citation by the National Book Award Committee for his *poems 1923-1954*, the Bollingen Prize in 1957 and a
Ford grant in 1959.

DAY LEWIS, C.   *The Unexploded Bomb*

C. DAY LEWIS was born in Ireland in 1901 where his father was
minister of the Church of Ireland. When he was two, his family
moved to England. Educated at Oxford University, he shared
the literary and political convictions of W. H. Auden, Louis

148

MacNeice, and Stephen Spender. At one time a member of the Communist party, he quit in disgust in 1939. During World War II he edited books and pamphlets for the Ministry of Information. From 1951-56 he was Professor of Poetry at Oxford University; in 1963 he was Charles Eliot Norton Professor at Harvard and also lectured at many American colleges. His *Selected Poems* (1967) draws material from his eleven previously published books of poetry. Honored in England and abroad, he is England's poet laureate, Vice-President of the Royal Society of Literature and a member of the American Academy of Arts and Letters. C. Day Lewis has also made a translation of the *Aeneid* and under the pseudonym of Nicholas Blake is an acknowledged writer of mysteries. He is presently a director of the English publishing house of Chatto, Boyd, and Oliver, Ltd. and lives in London.

DEUTSCH, BABETTE   *Ombres Chinoises*

BABETTE DEUTSCH was born in New York City and has spent much of her life there. Her writing first appeared in *The New Republic* while she was still an undergraduate at Barnard College. Her *Collected Poems* draws material from her eight books of poetry and covers from 1919 to 1969. She has also written biographies of the French poet, François Villon, and the American poet, Walt Whitman; two critical books, *Poetry in Our Time* (1963) and *Poetry Handbook* (1962); and several books for children. She and her husband Avrahm Yarmolinsky have translated the work of Russian poets from Pushkin to Yevtushenko. For many years she has given a course in twentieth century poetry at Columbia.

DICKEY, JAMES   *Sun*
                              Cherrylog Road
                    Encounter in the Cage Country
                                   The Jewel

JAMES DICKEY was born in 1923 in Georgia where he grew up. In 1943 he became a pilot in the Pacific where he was twice awarded the Distinguished Flying Cross and the Silver Star. After the war he returned to the South, graduating from Vanderbilt University in 1948 with high honors. In 1950 Vanderbilt granted him an M.A. before he was recalled to active duty in Korea where he once again served with distinction. He has made numerous college campuses his home either as teacher or poet-in-residence. He has won some ten grants and fellowships including the National Book Award in 1966 and published seven books of verse of which *Poems 1957-1967* is his most recent collection. In addition, he has established a reputation as a critic in such books as *The Suspect in Poetry* (1964) and *Babel to Byzantium, Poets and Poetry Today A Critical Study* (1968). His private interests include hunting with bow and arrow, guitar playing and collecting, world literature (in four languages) and travel. James Dickey now lives in Leesburg, Virginia with his wife and two sons.

DUGAN, ALAN   *Portrait*

ALAN DUGAN was born in 1923 in Brooklyn and graduated from Mexico City College. Married to the painter Judith Shahn and currently a member of the faculty of Sarah Lawrence, he has published three volumes of verse: *Poems* (1961), *Poems 2*, (1963), and *Poems 3* (1967). *Poems* received both the Pulitzer Prize and the National Book Award.

DURRELL, LAWRENCE   *Water Music*

LAWRENCE DURRELL, a British citizen of Irish parentage, was born in the Himalayas in India in 1912 and attended school there until he was ten. After that he studied in England and spent large portions of his youth in Corfu in the Mediterranean. His easy familiarity with Greek and his fondness for the Mediterranean inspired two of his books, *Prospero's Cell* and *Reflections on a Marine Venus*. In addition to these works he is one of the best known modern novelists. He has received particular literary acclaim for *The Alexandria Quartet*. His latest works are *Tunc* and *The Spirit of Place*. Besides his wide ranging literary activities, he has pursued a lively diplomatic career during which he served for three years as Director of Public Relations for the Government of Cyprus. From this experience he wrote his prize-winning *Bitter Lemons* (1958). As if these activities were insufficient, he has taught, traveled widely, and published his poetry in numerous journals in both England and the United States. His books of poetry include *Collected Poems* (1960) and *Ikons and Other Poems* (1967) as well as a critical work *Key to British Poetry* (1952).

EBERHART, RICHARD   *A Maine Roustabout*

RICHARD EBERHART was born in Austin, Minnesota. He studied
at the University of Minnesota, graduated from Dartmouth, and
did graduate work at Cambridge University in England. He has
led a life of many facets: Harvard instructor, tutor to the son
of the King of Siam, Lt. Cmdr. in the U.S. Navy during World
War II, vice-president of the Butcher Polish Company in Boston,
founder of the Poet's Theatre in Cambridge, Massachusetts, Consultant in Poetry to the Library of Congress, advisor to the
John F. Kennedy Cultural Center in Washington, and since
1956, Professor of English and now poet-in-residence at Dartmouth. *Selected Poems, 1939-1965* is his choice from his seven
books of poetry, and *Collected Verse Plays* (1962) is a survey
of his dramatic writings. In addition, he published *Thirty-One
Sonnets* in 1967 and *Shifts of Being* in 1968. He compiled with
Selden Rodman an anthology, *War and the Poet* (1945), has
written pieces of criticism, and recorded his poetry. This distinguished career has won him an Hon. L.D.D. from Dartmouth,
the Shelley Memorial Prize, the Bollingen Prize, and a grant by
the National Institute of Arts and Letters. Appropriately, in addition to swimming, cruising, and tennis, Richard Eberhart likes
to fly giant kites.

FROST, ROBERT   *Range-Finding*
                             Acquainted with the Night

ROBERT FROST was born in San Francisco, California in 1874. His
parents came from old New England stock. After his father's
death when he was ten, his mother moved to Lawrence, Massachusetts. During his teens he helped support the family by working in a shoeshop, textile mill, and on a local newspaper. Formal
education, including a brief period at Dartmouth and Harvard,
failed to stir his enthusiasm; he soon became a New Hampshire
farmer. The farm did not produce; Frost turned to teaching and
then decided to go to England and write poetry. His first book
of poems, *A Boy's Will*, appeared when he was forty and farm-
ing in England. His second book of poems, *North of Boston*
(1915) brought him great acclaim. Returning to the United
States, he bought another farm and thenceforth supported himself by lecturing, serving as poet-in-residence at various colleges,
and writing eight books of poetry which include his *Selected
Poems* (1954) and *Pod of Milkweed* published when he was
eighty-eight. His fresh, clear, vigorous style, like the New Eng-

land countryside and character he wrote about, won him the Gold Medal of the National Institute of Arts and Letters and four Pulitzer Prizes. An admirer of clarity and symmetry, he said: "I'd as soon write free verse as play tennis with the net down." A courageous man, he read his poem *Mending Wall* to the Russians in Moscow shortly after the Berlin Wall was put up. Awarded honorary degrees by twenty-eight colleges, honored by Vermont's naming a mountain after him, invited before the U.S. Senate, and asked to read one of his poems at the inauguration of John Fitzgerald Kennedy, his death in 1963 brought, as President Kennedy said, "a vacancy in the American spirit."

GRAVES, ROBERT

From the Embassy
Nobody

ROBERT GRAVES was born in London in 1895. Educated at Charterhouse, he won a scholarship to Oxford but joined the Royal Fusiliers instead. His experience in World War I of the devastations of trench warfare led him to write *Goodbye to All That*, an autobiographical account of the schoolboy-soldiers of that war. After the war he married, studied at Oxford, and supported himself by running a shop. Famed as a Classics scholar, he has had a wide career. His research into classical mythology produced his influential studies *The Greek Myths; The White Goddess*, a study of the pagan world and the origins of poetry; and translations of *The Iliad* and *The Golden Ass*. One of his latest translations, the *Rubaiyat of Omar Khayyam* in 1968 was a complete break from the long accepted version and caused a scholarly ruckus. His historical novels, particularly *I, Claudius*, have been widely acclaimed. He has also written books of criticism such as *The Crowning Privilege*, an attack on obtuse poets. His *Collected Poems* (1955) received both the Gold Medal of the National Poetry Society and the Foyle Award in England. In 1961 he was elected to the Chair of Poetry at Oxford University. He believes that: "Poetry is more than words, musically arranged. It is sense; good sense; penetrating, often heart-rending sense." His latest poetry books include *New Poems* (1963), *Man Does, Woman Is* (1964), and *Love Respelt* (1965) published on his seventieth birthday. Robert Graves and his second wife live on the island of Majorca.

GREGORY, HORACE

Spyglass

HORACE GREGORY was born in Milwaukee, Wisconsin in 1898. In 1923 he received his B.A. in Classics from the University of Wisconsin. His fascination with Latin verse led him to translate *The Poems of Catullus* (1931), *Ovid's Metamorphoses* (1958) and *Love Poems of Ovid* (1964) and to teach classical literature as well as modern poetry from 1934 to his retirement in 1960 from Sarah Lawrence College. He has published numerous books of poetry including *Poems 1930-1940*, *Medusa in Gramercy Park* (1961) and *Alphabet for Joanna* (1968). In addition, he has written a critical study of D. H. Lawrence; biographies of Amy Lowell, James MacNeill Whistler, and Dorothy Richardson; and edited writings of Sherwood Anderson, Robert Browning, and Henry Wadsworth Longfellow. With his wife, the poet Marya Zaturenska, he has produced *A History of American Poetry 1900-1940*, two anthologies of poetry for young readers, *The Crystal Cabinet: An Invitation to Poetry* (1962) and *Silver Swan: Poems of Mystery and Romance* (1966) and the *Mentor Book of Religious Verse*. His work has won him the Bollingen Award for his *Collected Poems* (1965) as well as awards from The National Institute of Arts and Letters and The Academy of American Poets. He and his wife live near New York City.

GUNN, THOM

A Trucker
Rastignac at 45

THOM GUNN was born in England in 1929 and came to the United States in 1954 where he has lived mostly in San Francisco. He has published four books of poetry, *Fighting Teams* (1954), *The Sense of Movement* (1957), *My Sad Captains* (1961), and *Touch* (1967). He and his brother Ander Gunn joined their talents on *Positives* (1966), a book of Thom Gunn's poems illustrated by his brother's photographs. The poet has been a lecturer at the University of California at Berkeley.

HALL, DONALD

The Assassin
An Adventure with a Lady
The Old Pilot's Death
Self-Portrait as a Bear

DONALD HALL was born in New Haven in 1928; he was educated at Exeter, Harvard, and Oxford University. His first book of poems, *Exiles and Marriages*, was the 1955 Lamont Poetry Selection of the Academy of American Poets. In 1958 he published his second collection, *The Dark Houses*, in 1964 *A Roof of Tiger Lilies*, and in 1969 *The Alligator Bride: poems new and selected*. He has also written an account of his New England childhood, *String Too Short To Be Saved* (1961) and a biography of *Henry Moore* (1966). He has compiled nine anthologies, notably *New Poets of England and America* (1957) and a second selection (1962) with Louis Simpson and Robert Pack, and *A Concise Encyclopedia of English and American Poetry and Poets* (1963) with Stephen Spender. He is now teaching English at the University of Michigan and serving as editorial consultant for Harper and Row.

HARRIS, PHYLLIS MASEK   *Furniture*

PHYLLIS MASEK HARRIS was born in 1940 in Gering, Nebraska. Prior to getting her B.A. degree at Loretto Heights College, she studied with the Institute of European Studies in Vienna. In 1964 she received her M.A. from San Francisco State College. Married and with a daughter, Phyllis Harris describes her current activities as "working as a tapestry-maker and student of Christianity."

HECHT, ANTHONY   *Lizards and Snakes*

ANTHONY HECHT was born in New York City and has taught at Bard College and at the University of Rochester. His first book of poetry, *A Summoning of Stones*, was published in 1954 and his second book, *The Hard Hours*, won the Pulitzer Prize in 1968. He and John Hollander have also collaborated on a book of poems entitled *Jiggery-Pokery* (1967). He is a Fellow of the American Academy in Rome and has received awards from the Guggenheim Foundation, the Ford Foundation and the National Academy of Arts and Letters.

HETRICK, LAWRENCE   *Arrowhead Field*

LAWRENCE HETRICK was born in 1940 in Williamsburg, Virginia and grew up in northern Florida. His mother and father are both biologists. "They nurtured in me," he has written, "a strong response to the natural world, but I did not respond in terms of science but in terms of poetry." Lawrence Hetrick's poems have been published in a number of poetry magazines and he is currently teaching a course in the writing of poetry at the University of Florida.

HOWES, BARBARA   *City Afternoon*

BARBARA HOWES, a native Bostonian, attended Bennington College and then came to New York where she edited the literary quarterly, *Chimera*, for four years. She is the author of four books of poems: *The Undersea Farmer* (1948), *In the Cold Country* (1954), *Light and Dark* (1959) and *Looking up at Leaves* (1966). She has won several awards including a Guggenheim Fellowship. She now lives in North Pownal, Vermont with her family.

HUGHES, LANGSTON   *Ballad of the Landlord*
                                                       As I grew Older
                                                              Harlem
                                                     Trumpet Player

LANGSTON HUGHES was born in Joplin, Missouri in 1902. He lived first with his grandmother in Kansas, then with his mother in Illinois, and after graduation from high school, a year with his father in Mexico. His father managed to send him to Columbia University, but after a year the money ran out. He then supported himself as a dish washer, seaman on freighters bound for Europe, cook in a Montmartre nightclub, and finally as a busboy in a New York restaurant. Discovering the poet Vachel Lindsay in the restaurant, Hughes dropped several poems on Lindsay's table. Lindsay was impressed with the quality of the works and demanded the identity of the author. Langston Hughes' poetry career was launched. One of the poems, "The Weary Blues," became the title of his first book of poetry published in 1925 which won him a scholarship to Lincoln University in Pennsylvania. He graduated in 1929 and in 1943 Lincoln awarded him an honorary Litt. D. The output of Langston Hughes was extensive: three dozen books on a wide range of fields. Of his work he said, "My writing has been largely concerned with the depicting of Negro life in America" and his poems, plays, short stories, novels, newspaper columns, and anthologies all bear witness to his talent and dedication. He translated the work of Negro writers in Cuba and Haiti as well. His last two books, published after his death in 1967, were a book of poems, *The Panther and the*

155

Lash, and *Black Magic,* a history of Negro performers in the United States. His other works include *Shakespeare in Harlem* (1960), *Black Nativity* (1961), *Selected Poems* (1959) and his last anthology, *Best Short Stories of Negro Writers* (1967).

IGNATOW, DAVID

Simultaneously
For One Moment

DAVID IGNATOW was born in Brooklyn and has spent most of his time in New York City. On finishing high school in the middle of the Depression, he supported himself as a WPA writer, a civil service clerk, shipyard worker, hospital clerk, and office manager in a bookbindery. A portrayer of the urban scene, his books of poetry are: *Poems* (1948), *The Gentle Weight Lifter* (1955), *Say Pardon* (1961), *Figures of the Human* (1964), and *Rescue the Dead* (1968). He has been editor of numerous poetry journals, critic, and teacher. He has received a grant from the National Institute of Arts and Letters as well as the Shelley Memorial Award. Currently, he is the editor of *Chelsea.*

JARRELL, RANDALL

A Pilot from the Carrier
The Metamorphoses

RANDALL JARRELL was born in 1914 in Nashville, Tennessee. He took both his B.A. and M.A. at Vanderbilt and was teaching at the University of Texas until he became a celestial navigator and tower operator for the Air Force in Europe during World War II. After the war he taught English at a number of American universities, served as Poetry Consultant to the Library of Congress and as poetry critic for various magazines. His seven books of verse include *The Woman in the Washington Zoo* (1961), *The Lost World* (1965), and *Complete Poems* (1968). In addition, he wrote a critical book, *Poetry and the Age* (1953); a book of essays, *A Sad Heart at the Supermarket* (1962); a novel; two books for children; and a translation of Chekhov's *The Three Sisters.* A member of the National Institute of Arts and Letters and winner of the National Book Award, he still felt that the poet went unnoticed in modern society, writing: "The public has an unusual relationship to the poet, it doesn't even know that he is there." In 1965 he was killed in a car accident while teaching at the University of North Carolina.

JUSTICE, DONALD   *The Missing Person*

DONALD JUSTICE is a native of Florida and a graduate of the University of Miami. He also holds advanced degrees from the Universities of North Carolina and Iowa. His first book of poems, *The Summer Anniversaries*, was the Lamont Poetry Selection for 1959. He has also written for the stage, edited the works of several poets, received a Rockefeller Fellowship in poetry, a Ford Fellowship in theater as well as the Harriet Monroe Prize and a grant from the National Council of the Arts. In 1967 he published his second book of poems, *Night Light*. Since 1966 Donald Justice has taught English at Syracuse.

KEROUAC, JACK   *121st Chorus*

JACK KEROUAC was born in Lowell, Massachusetts in 1922. Before his novel *On the Road* (1951) met with its fantastic literary success, Jack Kerouac spent six years "writing whatever came into my head, hopping freights, hitch-hiking, and working as a railroad brakeman, deckhand and scullion on merchant ships, government fire lookout, and hundreds of assorted jobs." His first and thus far only book of poems, *Mexico City Blues* (1959) reflects the wanderlust and adventures of these years. He has published four other novels, the latest *Vanity of Duluoz* (1968).

KILGORE, CRYSTAL   *On War*

CRYSTAL KILGORE's poem "On War" appeared in a newssheet which has subsequently been lost. We have made every effort to locate her with no success. We believe that she was a student in the New York City area in 1965. Should anyone have any information regarding her whereabouts we would be most grateful.

KINNELL, GALWAY   *First Song*

GALWAY KINNELL was born in Providence, Rhode Island in 1927 and brought up in nearby Pawtucket. In 1948 he received his A.B. summa cum laude from Princeton University and his M.A. from the University of Rochester a year later. Since that time he has taught in New York, Chicago, Grenoble, France and the University of Teheran, Iran. He has been the recipient of both an award from the National Institute of Arts and Letters and a Guggenheim Fellowship. His published books of poetry include

157

What a Kingdom It Was (1960), *Flower Herding on Mount Monadnock* (1964) and *Body Rags* (1968). Galway Kinnell has also published a novel *Black Light* (1966). In addition to these achievements, he has translated the complete work of François Villon, the fifteenth century French poet. At present he lives in New York City.

LANGLAND, JOSEPH   *War*
                                      Sacrifice of a Rainbow Trout

JOSEPH LANGLAND was born in Spring Grove, Minnesota of second generation Norwegian parents. He grew up in Iowa where he attended the University of Iowa. His two books of poetry have both received critical acclaim. *The Green Town* from *Poets of Today III* (1956) was a finalist for the National Book Award and *The Wheel of Summer* (1963) won the Melville Cane Award. Joseph Langland is also co-author of two anthologies: *The Short Story* with James B. Hall and *Poet's Choice* with Paul Engle. He is currently on the faculty of the University of Massachusetts.

LATTIMORE, RICHMOND   *American Nights*

RICHMOND LATTIMORE graduated from Dartmouth College, where he won a Rhodes Scholarship to Oxford University. Thereafter he completed an advanced degree at the University of Illinois. He has established a reputation as one of the foremost translators of the Greek classics, and in 1967 he won a National Book Award for his translation of Homer's *Odyssey*. He has published several books of poems of which the latest is *The Study of Time* (1966). In addition to his numerous awards he is a member of the National Academy of Arts and Letters. Richmond Lattimore is currently Professor of Greek at Bryn Mawr College in Pennsylvania.

LEVERTOV, DENISE   *Face to Face*
                                                    A Man

DENISE LEVERTOV was born in London in 1923 and grew up in Ilford, England. She was educated entirely at home (never attending school or college), studied ballet for a time and worked as a nurse during World War II. In 1947 she was married to the writer Mitchell Goodman and came to the United States the following year. With her husband and son she now lives in New York City. Denise Levertov's first book of poems *The Double Image* was published in England in 1946. She has since published in this country *Here and Now* in 1957, *Overland to the Islands* in 1958, *With Eyes at the Back of Our Heads* in 1960, *The Jacob's Ladder* in 1961, *O Taste and See* in 1964 and *The Sorrow Dance* in 1967. Like a number of other modern poets, Denise Levertov has not hesitated to enter the political arena. Both she and her husband have been frequent speakers on college campuses and have taken a particular interest in reform of the draft.

LOWELL, ROBERT

The Mouth of the Hudson
Fall 1961

ROBERT LOWELL, a descendant of the famed New England poets James Russell Lowell and Amy Lowell, was born in Boston, Massachusetts in 1917. He studied at Kenyon College, taking courses given by John Crowe Ransom, and taught there himself until he was drafted during World War II. Refusing to serve because of the American bombing of civilian populations, he was jailed. This courage to assert political beliefs led him to refuse an invitation to the White House Arts Festival in 1965 in protest against the Vietnam War. He is a well-established literary as well as a social critic. His poetry books include *Lord Weary's Castle*, the 1947 winner of the Pulitzer Prize; *The Mills of the Kavanaughs* (1951); *Life Studies*, the 1959 National Book Award; *Imitations* (1961); *For the Union Dead* (1964); and *Near the Ocean* (1966). He has also written *Old Glory, Endecott and the Red Cross* and other plays. His translation of Aeschylus' *Prometheus Bound* appeared in 1969. Winner of the Guinness Poetry Award and member of the American Academy of Arts and Letters, he bases his many activities in New York City, where he lives with his wife, the writer Elizabeth Harwick.

MAC LEISH, ARCHIBALD

What the Old Women Say

ARCHIBALD MAC LEISH was born in Glencoe, Illinois in 1892. In addition to a B.A. degree from Yale, he has received numerous advanced and honorary degrees from such institutions as Harvard, Columbia, and Dartmouth. During World War I he served in the Field Artillery. He was Director of the Office of Facts and Figures during World War II, one of President Roosevelt's confidential advisors, and eventually served as Assistant Secretary of State. After the war he worked with UNESCO and in 1957 he joined the faculty at Harvard. A controversial and influential voice, he has not hesitated to champion the value of contemporary poetry and has said, "Far from being an extinguished form of decorative writing that is going out of use, poetry is going to become an increasingly vital part of contemporary life." His literary enterprises are many. He has published a number of volumes of poetry: *Conquistador*, 1932 Pulitzer Prize winner; *Collected Poems 1917-1952*, winner of another Pulitzer; the National Book Award and the Bollingen Award; *Songs for Eve* (1954) and *The Wild Old Wicked Man and Other Poems* (1968). He is equally well known as a critic for such works as *Poetry and Experience* (1961) and the autobiographical *Continuing Journey* (1968); as a playwright for his Pulitzer Prize winning drama *J.B.*; and as one of America's eminent men of letters. In 1966 he was elected to the Academy of American Poets. He now lives in Conway, Massachusetts and winters in Antigua in the British West Indies.

MAC NEICE, LOUIS   *Brother Fire*

LOUIS MAC NEICE was born in Belfast, Ireland in 1907 and educated at Oxford University where he was associated with W. H. Auden, C. Day Lewis, and Stephen Spender. Although never as adamant in his social protest as they, his early poetry was involved with the issues of his times. In 1941 he joined the staff of the BBC as a script-writer and producer. Except for a year's leave of absence as Director of the British Institute in Athens in 1951, he remained with the BBC writing scripts including an abridged translation of Goethe's *Faust*. His books of poetry include *Ten Burnt Offerings* (1952), *Visitations* (1957), *Burning Perch* (1963) and *Collected Poems* (1967). He also wrote a study of the poet W. B. Yeats and collaborated with W. H. Auden on a book of their travels entitled *Letters from Iceland* (1937). Louis MacNeice died in 1963.

MATCHETT, WILLIAM H.   *Middle-Man*
                                                     Aunt Alice in April

WILLIAM H. MATCHETT was born in 1923 in Chicago, Illinois. He was educated at the Westtown School in Westtown, Pennsylvania, where he began writing poetry and also, as a Quaker, became a conscientious objector. After being drafted and doing alternate service, he received his B.A. from Swarthmore College and his M.A. and PhD. from Harvard University. Since 1954 William Matchett has taught at the University of Washington in Seattle where he is currently Professor of English. In 1954 he published his first book of poems, *Water Ouzel and Other Poems*. He is also the author of *The Phoenix and the Turtle* (1965), co-author with Jerome Beaty of *Poetry: From Statement to Meaning* (1965) and editor of the *Modern Language Quarterly*. William Matchett lives in Seattle, Washington with his wife and three children, is Clerk of the University Friends Meeting in Seattle, and is active with the American Friends Service Committee.

MATHEWS, JACK

Paradigm of a Hero
The Catfish

JACK MATHEWS was born in 1925 in Columbus, Ohio, where he grew up. He holds a B.A. in Classical Greek and English Literature and an M.A. in English Literature from Ohio State University. After serving in the Coast Guard during World War II, and working for ten years for the Post Office, he taught literature at Urbana College in Illinois from 1959 to 1964. In that year he published *Bitter Knowledge*, a book of short stories. In 1966 he published his first book of poems, *An Almanac for Twilight*. Currently Jack Mathews is a lecturer at Ohio University and lives in Athens, Ohio.

MC KUEN, ROD

Brownstone

ROD MCKUEN was born in Oakland, California at the end of the Depression. His life is characterized by energy and movement. He grew up in California, Oregon, Washington, and Nevada; worked as a laborer, stunt man, radio disk jockey, and newspaper columnist; served in Japan and Korea in psychological warfare; performed in Hollywood as an entertainer and actor; wrote, sang, and recorded some 700 folk ballads; composed and conducted his music on The CBS Workshop; toured this country and abroad performing his songs; and recently worked as a screen writer. In the midst of this peripatetic life, he has published three books of verse: *Stanyan Street and Other Sorrows* (1954), *Listen to the Warm* (1967) and *Lonesome Cities* (1968) and a collection of songs *The World of Rod McKuen* (1968). When not globetrotting, guitar in hand, he lives in the Hollywood hills surrounded by a menagerie of cats and dogs, writing, recording, and running a publishing and recording firm.

MEREDITH, WILLIAM   *The Fear of Beasts*

WILLIAM MEREDITH was born in 1919 in New York City and graduated from Princeton in 1940. During World War II he was a pilot in the Navy. When the war was over, he returned to Princeton where he taught English and Creative Writing. After once again serving in the Navy during the Korean War he taught at various universities. His first book of poems, *Love Letters from a Distant Land*, written while the poet was in the Aleutian Islands, was published in 1944 as a selection in the Yale Series of Younger Poets. Since then he has published *Ships and Other Figures* (1948), *The Open Sea* (1958) and *Wreck of the Thresher* (1964). He has won numerous awards and is currently Chancellor of the Academy of American Poets and a member of the National Institute of Arts and Letters. At present William Meredith is in Italy on leave of absence from Connecticut College.

MILLER, VASSAR   *Resolve*

VASSAR MILLER was born in Houston, Texas where she has spent most of her life. She graduated from the university there and has taught at Saint John's school in Houston. She has written poetry since childhood and her work has appeared in many periodicals. Her books of poetry include *Adam's Footprint* (1956), *Wage War on Silence* (1960), *My Bones Being Wiser* (1963) and *Onions and Roses* (1969). Originally a religious poet, Vassar Miller's poetry now probes all facets of life.

MOORE, MARIANNE   *What Are Years*

MARIANNE MOORE was born in Saint Louis, Missouri in 1887. On graduating from Bryn Mawr College, she taught at the Carlisle Indian School in Pennsylvania before coming to New York City to work as a librarian. Her official literary career began in 1925 when she joined the staff of *Dial* magazine. She has been influential in impressing her own poetic style on every decade since the twenties. She has been awarded every possible honor including the triple triumph of the Bollingen prize, the Pulitzer prize, and the National Book Award for her *Collected Poems* (1952). In

1953 she received the Gold Medal for Poetry from the National Institute of Arts and Letters and in 1968 a medal from the National Book Council for her continuing contribution. Her latest books include *Like A Bulwark* (1956), *O To Be a Dragon* (1959), *Tell Me, Tell Me: Granite, Steel and Other Topics* (1966), and *Complete Poems* (1967). She has also translated *The Fables of La Fontaine* and written a critical book on poetry, *Predilections* (1955). Since 1929 she has lived in Brooklyn.

MUELLER, LISEL

Names
Civilizing the Child

LISEL MUELLER was born in Germany and came to this country when she was fifteen. She holds a B.A. degree in sociology from Evansville College and has also studied folklore and social work at Indiana University and Loyola University of Chicago. Her first book of poems, *Dependencies*, was published in 1965. Her poems and literary criticism have appeared in a variety of magazines and literary journals. In 1968 Lisel Mueller's and John Reich's metrical translation of Hugo von Hofmansthal's verse play, *The Salzburg Great Theatre of the World*, was given its American premiere in Chicago. With her husband and two daughters Lisel Mueller now resides in suburban Chicago.

NEMEROV, HOWARD

The Daily Globe

HOWARD NEMEROV was born in 1920 in New York City. A graduate of Harvard, he served with the Royal Canadian Air Force and the United States Army Air Force during World War II. He has taught at various colleges and is presently at Brandeis University in Waltham, Massachusetts. A novelist and critic as well as a poet, Howard Nemerov has published four novels, one of which, *The Homecoming Game*, was made into the Broadway play and later the movie, *Tall Story*. His book *Poets on Poetry* (1967) is a series of essays by poets discussing their work. His own books of poetry include *Next Room of the Dream* (1963), *New and Selected Poems* (1963) and *The Blue Swallows* (1968) which received the first Roethke Memorial Poetry Award. Along with his many other activities, Howard Nemerov has served as Consultant in Poetry to the Library of Congress.

PACK, ROBERT
The Boat

ROBERT PACK was born in New York City in 1929 and educated at Dartmouth College and Columbia University. He has published three books of poetry: *The Irony of Joy* (1955), *A Stranger's Privilege* (1959) and *Guarded by Women* (1963) and written a number of books for children. In addition, he has been Poetry Editor for *Discovery* magazine, taught at the New School and Barnard College in New York City, compiled with Donald Hall and Louis Simpson *New Poets of England and America* (1957), and translated the librettos of Mozart's operas with Marjorie Lelash. He has been the recipient of a Fulbright Fellowship and a grant from the National Institute of Arts and Letters. He now lives with his wife in Connecticut.

PATCHEN, KENNETH
Always Another Viewpoint

KENNETH PATCHEN was born in Ohio in 1911 and attended the Experimental College at the University of Wisconsin. Although plagued by a chronic back condition, he has written numerous books of poetry, appeared with many jazz groups, recorded readings of poetry and been a key figure in forming contemporary poetic diction. His books of verse include *When We Were Here Together* (1957), *Because It Is* (1959), *But Even So* (1963), and *The Collected Poems* (1968). A number of his books also include drawings by the poet. In 1967 he was honored by the National Endowment for the Arts for "his life-long contribution to American letters." Kenneth Patchen and his wife live in Palo Alto, California.

PLATH, SYLVIA
Balloons
The Arrival of the Bee Box

SYLVIA PLATH was born in Boston in 1932. After her graduation from Smith College, she won a Fulbright Scholarship to Cambridge University, where she met her husband, the poet Ted Hughes. The year following their marriage, they taught at Smith and then returned to England to live. Her first book of poems, *The Colossus*, was published in 1960, the year of the birth of her first child. In 1962 a second child was born and the poetess turned to her writing with redoubled energy, working in the early dawn before her children awoke. In 1963 she committed suicide. *Ariel*, her second book of poems, was published after her death and received praise from all sides. Robert Penn Warren described this final work as "a keen, cold gust of reality as though somebody had knocked out a window pane on a brilliant night."

RANSOM, JOHN CROWE   *Good Ships*

JOHN CROWE RANSOM was born in Pulaski, Tennessee in 1888. He studied at Vanderbilt and then at Oxford as a Rhodes Scholar. Returning to Vanderbilt to teach, he formed with Allen Tate and Robert Penn Warren a poetry magazine called *The Fugitives* and under the fanciful pen name of Roger Prim wrote poetry. He left Vanderbilt for Kenyon College, where he stayed for twenty years as professor of poetry, founder and editor of *The Kenyon Review*, and leader of a group of poets and critics. His *Selected Poems* was published in 1963. His contribution to American poetry has won him wide acclaim including the Bollingen Prize, election to the National Academy of Arts and Letters, and in 1967 a grant from the National Endowment for the Arts.

REID, ALASTAIR   *The Day the Weather Broke*

ALASTAIR REID was born in Scotland in 1926 and lived there until he went into the Royal Navy during World War II. After the war he came to the United States where he taught at Sarah Lawrence College. His first collection of poems *To Lighten My House* appeared in 1953. His second book of poems, *Oddments, Inklings, Omens, Moments* was published in 1959 and the third *Passwords* in 1963. He has also written the librettos for six operas, scripts for movies, and several books for children. He now lives in Europe where he devotes most of his time to writing.

RICH, ADRIENNE   *Bears*
A Change of World
Aunt Jennifer's Tigers

ADRIENNE RICH was born in Baltimore, Maryland in 1929. While an undergraduate at Radcliffe College, she published in 1951 her first book of poems, *A Change of World,* in the Yale Series of Younger Poets. Since then she has published *The Diamond Cutters* (1955), *Snapshots of a Daughter-in-Law* (1963), *Necessities of Life* (1966) and *Leaflets* (1969). In addition, she has twice received a Guggenheim Fellowship and also been the recipient of an Amy Lowell Traveling Fellowship. She now lives with her family in New York and teaches at the School of the Arts at Columbia University and in the SEEK program at City College.

ROETHKE, THEODORE   *Night Journey*

THEODORE ROETHKE was born in 1908 and grew up in Saginaw, Michigan. He studied at both Michigan and Harvard Universities. For many years he taught English and coached tennis at a number of American universities. His numerous books of poetry include *Open House* (1941), *The Lost Son and Other Poems* (1948), *The Waking* (1953), *Praise to the End* (1951), *Words for the Wind* (1958), *I Am! Says the Lamb* (1961) and *The Far Field*, published posthumously in 1964. His lyrical and imaginative gifts won him a wide audience and numerous awards including a Pulitzer Prize and two National Book Awards. At his death in 1963, Theodore Roethke was living and lecturing in Seattle, Washington.

SANDBURG, CARL   *Mr. Attila*
The Long Shadow of Lincoln: A Litany

CARL SANDBURG was born in Galesburg, Illinois in 1878, the son of Swedish immigrant parents. His father, a blacksmith, signed his name with his "mark" because he had never been able to go to school. By the time Sandburg was thirteen he was working on a milktruck and before he was twenty he had "learned" the West as barber shop sweeper, theatre scene-shifter, pottery apprentice, truck driver, dishwasher, and harvest hand. As a journalist in the Spanish American War he earned enough to return to Galesburg and enter Lombard College. But formal education was not his style and once again he took to the road. While reporting for a Milwaukee newspaper, he met his wife, the sister of the photographer Edward Steichen. In 1912 he and his wife went to the city Sandburg was shortly to immortalize. With the publication of *Chicago Poems* in 1916, he found himself famous and controversial. His use of American slang shocked and challenged. His explanation was as simple and direct as the man himself: "There is formal poetry, only in form, all dressed up and nowhere to go . . . the number of syllables, the designated and unrelieved stresses of accent, the rhymes if wanted—they all come off with the skill of a solved crossword puzzle. Yet its animation and connotation are less than that of a dead mackerel in the moonshine."

Good Morning America (1928), *The People, Yes* (1936), and some seven other volumes have staked out Sandburg's claim as a major American poet. In 1950 his *Complete Poems* won the Pulitzer Prize. His fascination with Abraham Lincoln led ultimately to another Pulitzer Prize, this time for his four-volumed biography, *Lincoln: The War Years*. His other honors, including addressing a joint session of Congress, were extensive. Until his death in 1967, Carl Sandburg and his wife lived in North Carolina.

SCULLY, JAMES   *Lt. Cmdr. T. E. Sanderson*

JAMES SCULLY was born in New Haven in 1937 and educated at the University of Connecticut where he now teaches English. His poems have been published in the *New Yorker*, *Poetry*, and other magazines. His first book of poems, *The Marches*, appeared in 1967 and was widely praised. In 1962 he received an Ingram Merril Foundation Fellowship. He is currently the editor of *Modern Poetics*.

SEXTON, ANNE   *The Addict*
                                                    Kind Sir: These Woods

ANNE SEXTON was born in Newton, Massachusetts in 1928 where she grew up spending her summers on nearby Cape Cod and in Maine. Beginning with her first collection of poems, *To Bedlam and Part Way Back* in 1960, her highly confessional poetry has met with wide recognition and interest. Her second book, *All My Pretty Ones*, was written in 1962 while she was a Scholar with Radcliffe's New Institute for Independent Study. Her *Selected Poems* published in London in 1964 was a Poetry Book Society recommendation and *Live or Die* (1966) won the Pulitzer Prize for poetry. Her latest book, *Love Poems*, appeared in 1969. She has won grants from the American Academy of Arts and Letters, the Ford Foundation, the Congress for Cultural Freedom, and been made a Fellow of The Royal Society of Literature in London. Anne Sexton lives in Weston, Massachusetts with her husband and two daughters.

SHAPIRO, KARL   *The Leg*

KARL SHAPIRO was born in Baltimore, Maryland in 1913 and educated at the University of Virginia and Johns Hopkins University.

His book of poems about his experiences during World War II, *V-Letter and Other Poems*, won the Pulitzer Prize in 1945. He has published five books of poems since then, including *Poems of a Jew* (1958), *The Bourgeois Poet* (1964), *The White-Haired Lover* (1968), and *Selected Poems* (1968). An avid experimenter with poetic forms, his style has constantly changed. In 1969 he shared the Bollingen Prize with John Berryman; he is also a member of the National Institute of Arts and Letters. His career has taken him to many colleges. Currently, he is Professor of English at the University of California at Davis.

SIMPSON, LOUIS   *The Battle*

LOUIS SIMPSON was born in Jamaica, British West Indies, the son of a lawyer and an actress. Receiving his B.S., M.A., and Ph.D. degrees from Columbia University, he taught there for several years before becoming an editor in a publishing house. He then returned to teaching first at the University of California at Berkeley and now at Stony Brook, New York where he lives with his wife and children. His first book of poetry, *The Arrivists*, was published in 1949. *Good News of Death* appeared in 1955, *A Dream of Governors* in 1959, and the Pulitzer Prize winner *At the End of the Open Road* in 1963. Louis Simpson published his *Selected Poems* in 1965 and in 1967 a critical study and anthology, *Introduction to Poetry*. In collaboration with Donald Hall and Robert Pack, he has also compiled the anthology, *New Poets of England and America*. A novelist and biographer as well, Louis Simpson has received many honors, including the Prix de Rome, acceptance as a Fellow of the American Academy of Arts and Letters and a Fellow of the John Guggenheim Memorial Foundation.

SPENDER, STEPHEN   *Air Raid across the Bay of Plymouth*

STEPHEN SPENDER was born in London in 1909. By the time he was accepted in Oxford, he had made enough money to support himself by printing chemists' labels on his own printing press. His first book of poems, *Twenty Poems*, was published while he was still at Oxford where he formed lasting friendships with W. H. Auden, C. Day Lewis, and Louis MacNeice. Like his friends, his concern with political causes was reflected in his work. His book *The God That Failed* describes his disillusionment with the Communist Party which he idealistically joined in the thirties. *Poems for Spain* and *The Still Centre* appeared in

168

1939 while he was co-editor for the magazine *Horizon*. During World War II he served as a fireman in the N.F.S. and after the war he worked with UNESCO. In 1953 he helped establish the magazine, *Encounter*, with which he is still associated. Stephen Spender has taught in several colleges, received an Hon. D. Litt. from the University of Montpelier and an Hon. Mem. Phi Beta Kappa from Harvard. His *Collected Poems* was published in 1954 and *Selected Poems* in 1965. His critical works include *The Making of a Poem* (1955), and *The Struggle of the Modern* (1963). An autobiography, *World Within World* was published in 1951 and his translation of Schiller's *Mary Stuart* in 1958. With Donald Hall, he has compiled the anthology *Concise Encyclopedia of English and American Poets* (1963) and since 1965 he has been the Consultant in Poetry at the Library of Congress.

STAFFORD, WILLIAM   *The Woman from Banff*
                                              A Stared Story

WILLIAM STAFFORD was born in 1914 in Hutchinson, Kansas, where he lived until he was of high school age. His father's job as district manager for an oil company then moved the family from one Kansas town to another. The rigors of outdoor life and camping combined with the family evenings devoted to books and talk made Kansas for Stafford "a great good place." While he was studying at the University of Kansas, World War II began and he was drafted into a camp for conscientious objectors. Returning to college after the war, he received his M.A. from the University of Kansas, and his Ph.D. from the State University of Iowa. He also served as education secretary for the Church World Service, a relief organization in San Francisco. His first book of poetry, *West of Your City*, was published in 1960 followed by *Traveling through the Dark*, winner of the 1963 National Book Award, and *The Rescued Year* (1966). With his wife and four children, he now lives in Lake Oswego, Oregon where he teaches English Literature and composition at Lewis and Clark College in Portland, Oregon. A new collection of his poems *Earth Dweller* will be published in 1970.

STALLWORTHY, JON   *Out of Bounds*
                                               First Blood

JON STALLWORTHY was born near Oxford, England in 1935 and was educated at Rugby School and Oxford, where he won the Newdigate Prize for Poetry. He served his compulsory service with the Royal West African Frontier Force. His published books of verse include *The Astronomy of Love* (1961), *Out of Bounds* (1963), and *Root and Branch* (1969). In addition, he is the author of two critical books on W. B. Yeats: *Between the Lines— W. B. Yeats' Poetry in the Making* and *Vision and Revision in Yeats' Last Poems*. At present Jon Stallworthy lives in London where he is an editor for the Oxford University Press.

STANFORD, ANN   *The Riders*
                            An Anniversary: A Country Burial

ANN STANFORD was born and raised in California. Her poetry first appeared in Yvor Winters' *Twelve Poets of the Pacific* while she was an undergraduate at Stanford University. She received her Ph.D. from the University of California. She has published four books of poetry: *In Narrow Bound* (1943), *The White Bird* (1949), *Magellan: A Poem to be Read by Several Voices* (1959), and *The Weathercock* (1966). She has won several awards. Married, with three daughters, she lives in Beverly Hills, California and teaches English at San Fernando State College.

STEVENS, WALLACE   *The Man with the Blue Guitar*
                                      The Beginning
                                  Domination of Black

WALLACE STEVENS was born in Reading, Pennsylvania in 1879. He studied at Harvard and then took his law degree from New York Law School. After practicing in New York, he joined the Hartford Accident and Indemnity Insurance Company. Although a vice-president of the company, Stevens still pursued the writing of poetry. Unpublished until he was forty-four, he wrote six books of poetry including *The Man with the Blue Guitar* and his *Collected Poems* which received the National Book Award and the Pulitzer Prize in 1955, the year of his death. Wallace Stevens, a reserved man, said of his poetry: "Poetry is my way of making the world palatable. It's the way of making one's experience, almost wholly inexplicable, acceptable."

SWENSON, MAY   *The Contraption*
                                    Cause and Effect
                              Death Great Smoothener
                                      The Universe

MAY SWENSON was born in Logan, Utah and graduated from Utah State University where her father taught Mechanical Engineering. Shortly after graduation, she came to New York City. Her first collection of poems, *Another Animal*, appeared in 1954 in *Poets of Today, Number One. A Cage of Spines* followed in 1958 and in 1963 *To Mix with Time*. In 1965 she published a collection of poems for children, *Poems to Solve*, and in 1969, *Half Sun Half Sleep: New Poems*. She has also written several plays, been an editor at New Directions, served as judge for the Academy of American Poets and for the National Book Award, and been writer-in-residence at Purdue University. May Swenson has received a Guggenheim Fellowship, grants from the National Institute of Arts and Letters and the Ford Foundation, and the Shelley Award.

UPDIKE, JOHN   *Sonic Boom*
                                  Ex-Basketball Player

JOHN UPDIKE was born in Shillington, Pennsylvania where he attended public school before going to Harvard. After graduation he spent a year at Oxford in the Ruskin School of Drawing and Fine Art. From 1955 to 1957 he was a member of the editorial staff of *The New Yorker* where much of his work has appeared. His first volume of poetry, *The Carpentered Hen and Other Tame Creatures* was published in 1958, *Telephone Poles and Other Poems* in 1963, *Verse*, a collection of his work, in 1968 and *Midpoint and Other Poems* in 1969. In addition, he has established a reputation as an important contemporary novelist with such works as *Rabbit Run* (1960), *The Centaur* (1963), winner of the National Book Award, *The Poor House Fair* (1964), and *Couples* (1968). He has also been a prolific writer of short stories. With his wife and two children, John Updike now lives in Ipswich, Massachusetts.

VALENTINE, JEAN   *To a Friend*

JEAN VALENTINE was born in Chicago in 1934. When she was three, her family moved to the East, eventually settling in Cambridge, Massachusetts. Since graduation from Radcliffe College, she has lived in New York City writing poetry and raising her two children. Her first book of poems, *Dream Barker*, was the Yale Series of Younger Poets selection for 1965 and her second book, *Pilgrims*, was published in 1969. She has given readings at many schools and is presently teaching a workshop poetry course at Swarthmore College. Her other honors include a grant from the Radcliffe Institute.

VAN DOREN, MARK *The Cat and the Miser*

MARK VAN DOREN was born in Hope, Illinois in 1894. Until 1915 he remained in Illinois where he attended the University of Illinois from which he received both a B.A. and M.A. degree. His M.A. thesis on Henry Thoreau had the unusual distinction of being commercially published. After two years in the U.S. Army during World War I, he returned to Columbia University, received his doctorate there in 1920, and once again had his dissertation—this time on the English poet John Dryden—published and widely praised. From then on Mark Van Doren followed a career composed of teaching, writing, and editing. He remained at Columbia where he earned an international reputation as a Shakespeare scholar and teacher; he acted as both literary editor and movie critic for *The Nation* and he established his reputation as poet, critic, and playwright. Mark Van Doren has published some sixteen volumes of poetry including *Collected Poems*, for which he won the Pulitzer prize in 1939, and *Mark Van Doren: 100 poems*, his own selected poems, in 1967. Mark Van Doren's honors are numerous; he has won awards from the American Academy of Arts and Sciences and the Academy of American Poets, to mention but two. Mark Van Doren and his wife now live in Falls Village, Connecticut.

WAGONER, DAVID *The Hold-Up*

DAVID WAGONER was born in Massillon, Ohio and grew up in Whiting, Indiana. He received his B.A. in 1947 from Penn State and his M.A. from Indiana University. His fifth book of poems, *New and Selected Poems*, was published in 1969 and his fifth novel, *Baby, Come On Inside* was published in 1968. He received a grant from the National Institute of Arts and Letters in 1967. He is currently editor of *Poetry Northwest* and Professor of English at the University of Washington.

WHEELOCK, JOHN HALL *The Black Panther*

JOHN HALL WHEELOCK's eighty-two years stand as a monument of poetic accomplishment. Born in Long Island in 1886; his first poem, a paraphrase of Ovid's *Metamorphoses*, appeared anonymously in the local newspaper. Four years later, as a freshman at Harvard, he and Van Wyck Brooks jointly published *Verses by Two Undergraduates*. On his graduation from Harvard in 1908, he spent three years studying in Germany before joining the publishing firm of Charles Scribner's Sons with whom he remained until his retirement in 1957. During those years he first published a number of the contributors to this volume, including May Swenson, Robert Pack, Louis Simpson and James Dickey. In addition, he is the author of ten books of verse, the most recent being *Dear Men and Women* (1966), *The Gardener and Other Poems*, a co-winner of the 1961 Bollingen Prize, and *Poems Old and New* (1956). He is also the author of a book of critical thought, *What Is Poetry?* His awards are many and include membership in The National Institute of Arts and Letters as well as being Chancellor of The Academy of American Poets.

WILBUR, RICHARD
A Fire-Truck
Statues

RICHARD WILBUR was born in New York City in 1921 and grew up on a farm in New Jersey. On graduation from Amherst College, he served two years overseas in the Army during World War II. After receiving his M.A. from Harvard, he turned to teaching, first at Harvard, then at Wellesley, and presently at Wesleyan University where he has been Professor of English since 1957. He has published some five books of poetry including *The Poems of Richard Wilbur* (1963) and *Walking to Sleep* (1969). An earlier volume of verse, *Things of This World* (1956) won the Pulitzer Prize, the National Book Award, and the Edna St. Vincent Millay Memorial Prize. He has retained tradition verse forms such as rhyme and meter believing, "The Strength of the genie comes of his being confined in a bottle." In addition to his achievement as an original poet, he has done notable verse translations of various French poets and particularly of two Molière plays, *Tartuffe* and *The Misanthrope*.

WILSON, KEITH
guerilla camp

KEITH WILSON was born in 1927 in Clovis, New Mexico. He grew up in the Southwest, punching cows, digging ditches, working on farms and ranches. He attended fifteen grammar schools and three high schools following his engineer father about the Southwest. In 1945 he entered the United States Naval Academy from which he graduated in 1950. The next four years he served at sea, largely in Korea. In 1954 he resigned his commission and entered the University of New Mexico where he received his M.A. in literature in 1956. The next two years he worked as a technical writer before he became a university instructor. Currently Keith Wilson is an assistant professor of English at New Mexico State University. He lives in the small Mexican-American village of San Miguel with his wife, four children, two dogs, and three cats. His books of poems are: *Sketches for a New Mexico Hill Town* (1966), *Sequences* (1967), *The Old Car and Other Black Poems* (1968), *Graves Registry* (1969), and *The Shadow of Our Bones* (1969). His work is also represented in *31 New American Poets* (1969).

WRIGHT, JAMES   *To A Fugitive*
                        A Note Left in Jimmy Leonard's Shack
                                                    Autumnal

JAMES WRIGHT was born and spent his youth in Martins Ferry, Ohio. He graduated from Kenyon College, and then went on to Vienna, Austria as a Fulbright scholar before returning to the University of Washington for his M.A. and Ph.D. He has taught at the University of Minnesota, Macalaster in Minnesota, and since 1966 at Hunter College in New York City. He has published four books of poetry including *The Green Wall* (1956), *Saint Judas* (1959), and *Shall We Gather at the River* (1968). In addition, he has translated modern German and Spanish poets. His work has won a number of awards including the Robert Frost Prize and a grant from the National Institute of Arts and Letters.

ZATURENSKA, MARYA   *Flight of the Sparrows*
                                                Girl's Song

MARYA ZATURENSKA was born in Kiev, Russia and came to the United States when she was eight. Her poems appeared in magazines before she had graduated from the University of Wisconsin. She has written six books of poems, including *Cold Morning Sky*, the 1938 Pulitzer Prize winner, and *Collected Poems* (1965). She has also written a biography of Christina Rossetti, edited the works of Sara Teasdale, and collaborated with her husband, the poet Horace Gregory, on *A History of American Poetry 1900-1940* and on several anthologies, notably *The Crystal Cabinet: An Invitation to Poetry* (1962) and *Silver Swan: Poems of Mystery and Romance* (1966).